Books have everything—
　　　Bluebirds singing tunes,
　　　　　Reindeer cartoons,
　　　　　　　Silly pigs as balloons!

Some stories are funny
　　　And some are sad,
　　　　　Some will amaze you,
　　　　　　　Others make you glad!

The stories inside
　　　Are there just for you,
　　　　　So hop, skip, and jump
　　　　　　　t h r o u g h

HOUGHTON MIFFLIN
The Literature Experience
READING

COME ONE, COME ALL.

Senior Author
John J. Pikulski

*Senior Coordinating
Author*
J. David Cooper

*Senior Consulting
Author*
William K. Durr

Coordinating Authors
Kathryn H. Au
M. Jean Greenlaw
Marjorie Y. Lipson
Susan Page
Sheila W. Valencia
Karen K. Wixson

Authors
Rosalinda B. Barrera
Ruth P. Bunyan
Jacqueline L. Chaparro
Jacqueline C. Comas
Alan N. Crawford
Robert L. Hillerich
Timothy G. Johnson
Jana M. Mason
Pamela A. Mason
William E. Nagy
Joseph S. Renzulli
Alfredo Schifini

Senior Advisor
Richard C. Anderson

Advisors
Christopher J. Baker
Charles Peters

HOUGHTON MIFFLIN COMPANY   BOSTON
Atlanta   Dallas   Geneva, Illinois Palo Alto   Princeton   Toronto

Growing Up

BOOK 1

THEME BOOK
Molly and the Slow Teeth
by Pat Ross

Tomie dePaola

BOOK 2

THEME BOOK
The Quicksand Book
by Tomie dePaola

Aesop's Fables

BOOK 3

THEME BOOK
Once in a Wood:
Ten Tales from Aesop
retold by Eve Rice

194

IN and OUT of TROUBLE

BOOK 4

THEME BOOK
Mouse Soup
by Arnold Lobel

GLOSSARY
258

Growing Up

As you grow up, you get bigger, taller, and stronger. You also learn new things and do new things. Every day, in some way, you grow and change.

In this book, you will read stories about boys and girls just like you. They too are growing up.

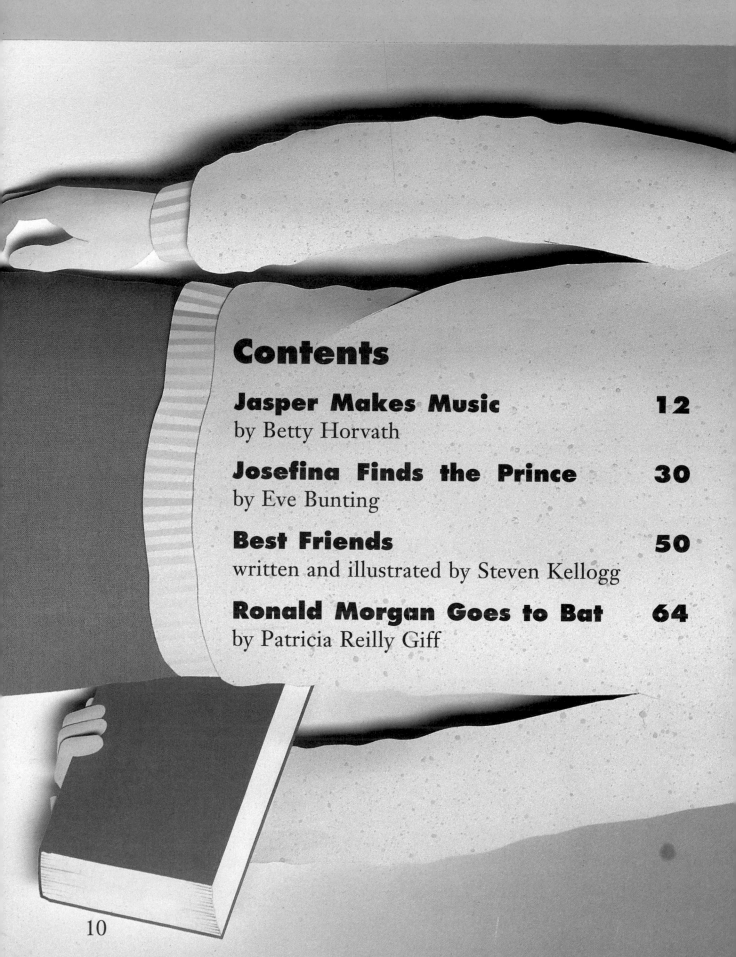

Contents

Jasper Makes Music

Written by Betty Horvath

Illustrated by Floyd Cooper

Jasper wanted a guitar — a real guitar of his own that he could carry around and strum and make music with. He had wanted it for a long time. Then he saw the guitar in the window of Anderson's Music Store and he knew suddenly and certainly that this was the *very* guitar he wanted. He had to have it.

But tied to the neck of the guitar was a price tag. It said $29.95. In all Jasper's eight years he had never had that much money. Right now he didn't have *any*.

He turned his pockets inside out hopefully. One pocket held a gum wrapper and a piece of string, and the other had nothing in it but a sticky cough drop. No money at all. Not a single penny. Jasper pressed his face against the window until his nose was squashed flat, and he looked and looked.

All the way home he
thought about the guitar.
He hummed a little, and
his fingers made
strumming movements.

"If I had that old
guitar," he told himself,
"I could sit out on the
front-porch steps and
watch the moon come
up, and sing."

He ran to find his
mother.

"There's something I
need," Jasper told her.

His mother looked at
Jasper's feet. "I'll bet I
can guess," she said. "You
need a new pair of shoes."

"No," said Jasper,
"that's not it. I need a
guitar."

His mother laughed.
"No, Jasper. You just
want a guitar. What you
need is shoes."

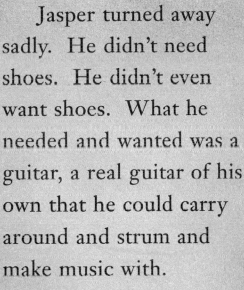

Jasper turned away
sadly. He didn't need
shoes. He didn't even
want shoes. What he
needed and wanted was a
guitar, a real guitar of his
own that he could carry
around and strum and
make music with.

Jasper went looking
for his father. He found
him up on a ladder
putting on storm
windows.

"Dad," Jasper called
up to him, "there's
something I need."

"There's something I
need, too, son," his father
said. "Run and get me
the hammer."

Jasper brought him
the hammer, and began
again. "There's something
I need. I need a guitar."

"A guitar?" His father grunted. "What do you need a guitar for?"

"To make music," Jasper said.

"We've got a radio for that," his father said, and he began hammering so loudly that Jasper couldn't tell him about the guitar in the window of Anderson's Music Store that looked as if it belonged to him.

"Maybe I can make a guitar," Jasper thought.

He found an empty cigar box, and his big brother Paul helped him nail a thin board to it for a neck. Then they strung it with rubber bands. Jasper took it out on the front-porch steps and started to sing and play. But no matter how hard he tried, he and his guitar just didn't seem to be singing the same song. It didn't sound like a guitar at all. It sounded like an old cigar box strung with rubber bands, and Jasper put it down.

A week went by. Jasper got a new pair of shoes.

A month went by. He got a winter jacket because it was getting colder now. Winter was coming. Most evenings it was too cold, anyway, for him to sit out on the front-porch steps and sing and watch the moon come up. But every day after school, no matter how cold it was, Jasper walked down to Anderson's Music Store to see if the guitar was still in the window. It always was.

One Saturday morning when Jasper woke up, he heard Grandpa's voice downstairs.

"Get up, Jasper! We've got work to do today."

Jasper dressed hurriedly. Working with Grandpa was a treat. He put on his oldest shirt and the blue jeans with patches, and clattered downstairs.

"What are we going to do today, Grandpa?" he asked.

Grandpa pointed out the window. "See those squirrels? They know winter is coming. They're busy storing up food for the winter, and that's what we're going to do, too. We're going to be squirrels."

Jasper thought about being a squirrel. He thought about Grandpa being a squirrel. He almost laughed out loud.

Then he saw that one whole corner of the kitchen floor was covered with jar after jar of tomatoes, corn, peas, beans, and peaches that his mother had been canning all summer long.

"I know!" he said, pointing. "These are our 'acorns' and we're going to store them in the cellar."

"Right!" said Grandpa. "But before we store our food away we've got a job to do. We have to clean the cellar out first."

He handed Jasper a broom, and he and Jasper went down the back steps into the cool, dim, cobwebby little room under the house.

They began to work. It was hard work sweeping the floor and dusting off all the shelves, but it was kind of like a treasure hunt, too. Jasper kept finding things he hadn't seen for a long time. He found his baseball that had been missing most of the summer. He found an old roller skate — some pieces of chalk — a few marbles. Then, over in the corner, Jasper saw the handle of something half hidden behind some boxes. When he pulled it out, he was holding a small shovel.

"Look what I found, Grandpa!" he shouted.

Grandpa picked it up. "Why, I believe you've found the magic shovel I gave your daddy when he was about your size."

"A magic shovel! What's magic about it?" Jasper asked, and his eyes were big with excitement.

"It's magic because you can get things you wish for with it. If I remember rightly, it got your daddy a bicycle."

"Oh, boy!" said Jasper, thinking about the guitar. "How does it work?"

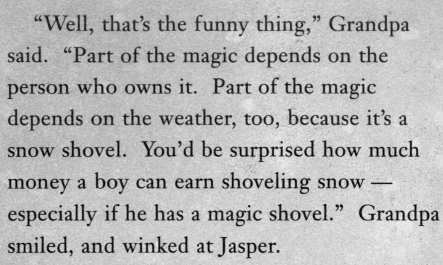

"Well, that's the funny thing," Grandpa said. "Part of the magic depends on the person who owns it. Part of the magic depends on the weather, too, because it's a snow shovel. You'd be surprised how much money a boy can earn shoveling snow — especially if he has a magic shovel." Grandpa smiled, and winked at Jasper.

Jasper winked back.

When they had finished storing all the jars in the cellar, Jasper polished his magic shovel until it shone. Then he stood it on the back porch to wait for the first snowy day.

While he was waiting, he made a few business calls.

Up and down the street he went, knocking on doors and asking his neighbors very politely if he could be their winter snow-shoveler.

"I've got a magic shovel," he told them, "and if I wish hard enough and work hard enough I'll earn enough money to buy a guitar."

Mrs. Adams said No, she didn't need a snow-shoveler.

Mrs. Hill said Maybe, sometimes.

Mr. Bixler said he did his own shoveling.

But Mrs. James and Miss Daniels and Mr. Arthur said Yes, Jasper could shovel their snow all winter long for fifty cents every single time it snowed. And of course Jasper told his mother that he would shovel free for his own family.

Then Jasper did one more thing. He needed a bank to keep his money in. He took an empty baking-powder can, covered it with white paper, and printed on it with a red crayon, GUITAR MONEY.

He was all ready for the first snowfall.

Then one day the snow began to fall.

It fell and fell and fell.
And Jasper shoveled
and shoveled and shoveled.
And he whistled while
he worked, because he
knew that by the time it

was warm enough again to
sit out on the front-porch
steps and sing, he'd have a
real guitar of his own to
carry around and strum
and make music with.

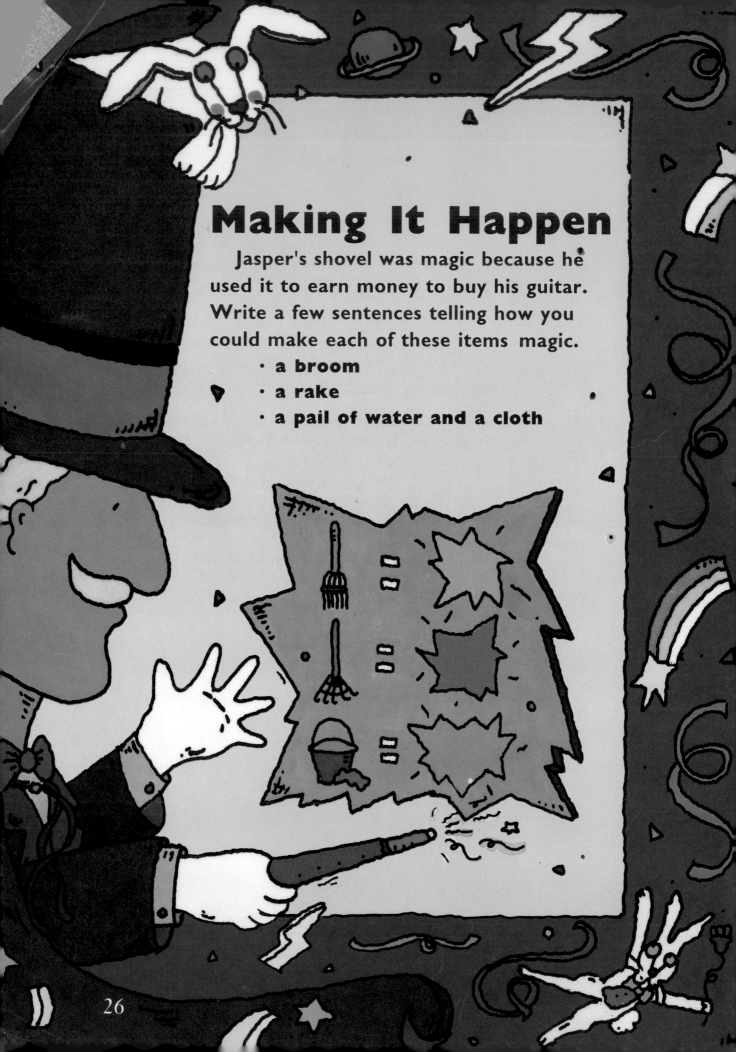

Making It Happen

Jasper's shovel was magic because he used it to earn money to buy his guitar. Write a few sentences telling how you could make each of these items magic.

- a broom
- a rake
- a pail of water and a cloth

Betty Horvath

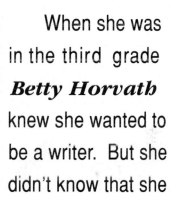

When she was in the third grade **Betty Horvath** knew she wanted to be a writer. But she didn't know that she would some day write especially for children. **Horvath** has said that many of the ideas for her children's books come from people and things in and around her **house.** But sometimes her stories seem to come from nowhere!

Here is another book about Jasper that you may enjoy reading, **Jasper and the Hero Business**. Jasper may not have to wait until he grows up to become a hero. Someone thinks , he is a hero now.

Whistles

I want to learn to whistle.
I've always wanted to.
I fix my mouth to do it but
The whistle won't come through.

I think perhaps it's stuck, and so
I try it once again.
Can people swallow whistles?
Where is my whistle then?

Dorothy Aldis

poem
for
rodney

people always ask what
am i going to be
when i grow
up and i always
just think
i'd like to grow
up

Nikki Giovanni

29

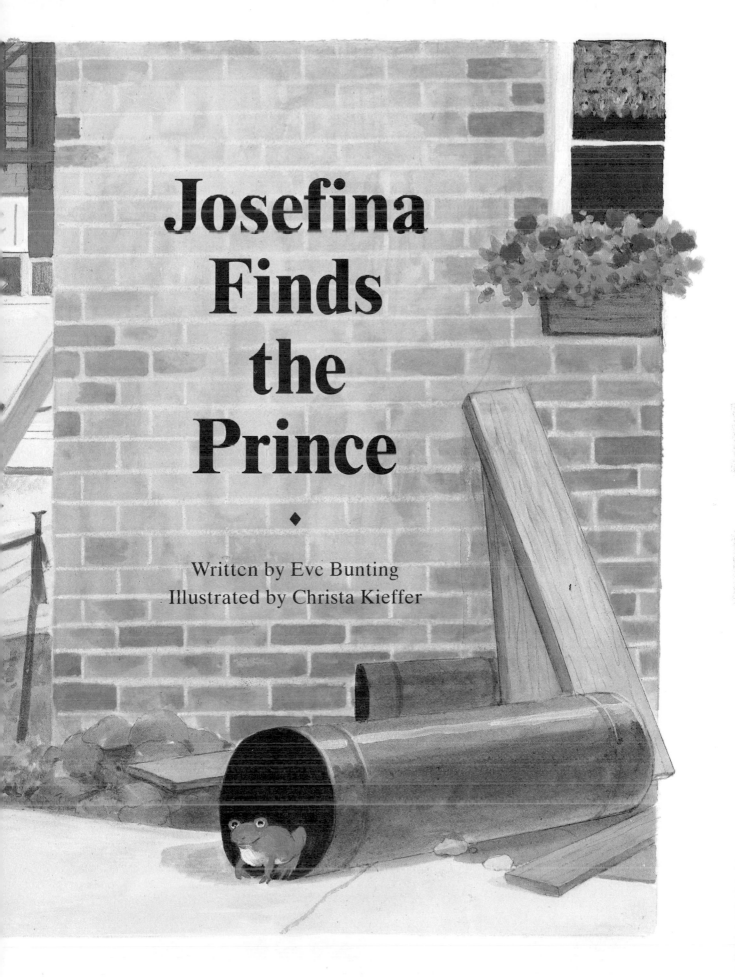

Josefina
Finds
the
Prince

◆

Written by Eve Bunting
Illustrated by Christa Kieffer

J osefina was walking to the park with her brother, Manuel. Manuel had his bat and ball.

"What's that?" Josefina asked.

CROAK! CROAK! CROAK! The sounds came from a big pipe.

Josefina looked inside the pipe. "It's a frog," she said.

"It can't be." Manuel walked on. "There are no frogs in the city."

"Here, frog! Here, frog!" Josefina called.

CROAK! CROAK! CROAK!

Manuel stopped. He looked in the pipe too. "It *is* a frog," he said. "But we can't get him out. The pipe is too long. He's too far inside."

The pipe was open at both ends.

"I know," Josefina said. "I'll push the frog from this end with your bat. You get him at the other end when he comes out."

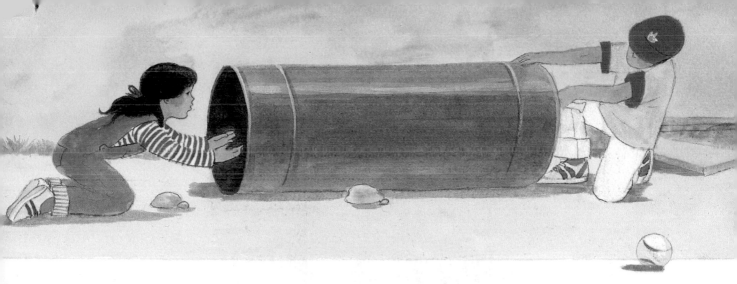

"OK," Manuel said. He put his bat in the pipe. "But *I'll* push. *You* get him when he comes out."

Josefina held out her hands. A cold, wet thing jumped into them. "I've got him," she said.

An old paper bag lay against a wall. "Get me the bag, Manuel," she called. "He's going to jump away."

Manuel held the bag. Josefina dropped the frog inside.

CROAK! CROAK! CROAK!

"He has to have air." Manuel made little holes in the bag.

"How did he get here?" Josefina asked.

"I don't know," Manuel said. "He may be a lost pet."

"Maybe he came from outside the city."

Manuel shook his head. "He couldn't hop that far."

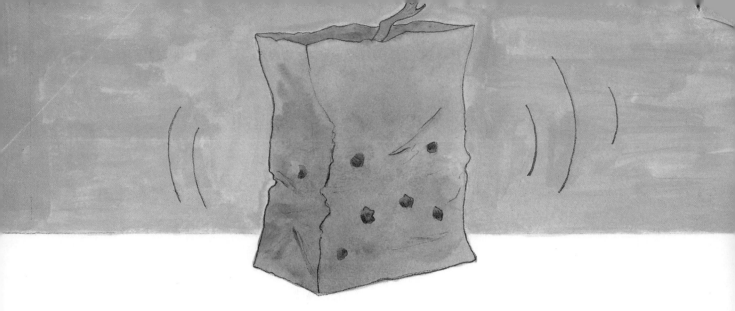

Josefina peeped into the bag.

CROAK! CROAK! CROAK! The frog jumped inside the bag.

"I have to go now," Manuel said. "I'll be late for my game."

"I have to go too." Josefina bit her lip. "I'll be late for the play reading. I want to try out for the princess part."

"Princess!" Manuel laughed. "You won't be the princess. The princess has golden hair. She has blue eyes. You don't look like a princess."

"I know," Josefina said. "But I'm going to try for the part anyway." She peeped in the bag again. "What will I do with the frog?"

"You should put him back in the pipe," Manuel said. "You can't take him to the play reading. And you can't take him home. The Señora will be mad."

The Señora owned the building where Josefina and Manuel lived with their mother. Sometimes the Señora was mean.

"She let us have Loco," Josefina said.

"Loco is a good cat. He keeps mice away. That's why she lets him stay." Manuel was walking away. "I tell you, she won't like a frog. You should put him back in the pipe."

CROAK! CROAK! CROAK! said Frog.

Josefina patted the bag. "Don't worry, Frog. I won't put you back. City streets are not safe for frogs. I'll find you a home."

Josefina walked to the pet shop. "Will you take a frog?" she asked the pet shop woman.

The woman shook her head. "We don't keep frogs. We have dogs and cats. We have fish and birds. But we don't keep frogs."

"What will I do with him?" Josefina asked.

"Give him to someone who has a yard," the pet shop woman said. "Frogs are good in yards. They eat the bugs."

"I don't know anyone who has a yard," Josefina said. "There aren't many yards in the city."

"I know," the woman said. "That's why we don't keep frogs."

Josefina walked slowly along the street. Policeman Tony stood by his police car. "I found a frog," Josefina told him. She held up the bag. "He's in here. Do you know who lost him?"

"No, I don't, Josie," Policeman Tony said. "If I find out, I'll let you know."

Josefina walked on. She passed the pipe where she had found the frog. "Don't worry, Frog," she said. "I won't put you back. City streets are not safe for frogs."

She tried not to think about the Señora. The Señora was not safe for frogs, but there was nothing else for Josefina to do. "I'll take you home," she said.

CROAK! CROAK! CROAK! said Frog.

Josefina took the bag home. Her mother was at work. Josefina was glad she didn't see the Señora.

Loco ran down the stairs to meet her. He smelled at the bag. "No, Loco," Josefina said. "Go away."

She went into the bedroom and opened the bag. In one jump, the frog was out.

"Come back, Frog," Josefina called.

Frog hopped on the mat.

Frog hopped on the chest.

Frog hopped on the bed.

He was as green as grass. His eyes were big and yellow. He had very long legs.

Josefina picked up her mother's big straw hat. She put it over the frog. "Now you can't hop away," she said. "I have to think."

Frog sat very still under the hat.

"Where did you come from, Frog?" Josefina asked.

The big hat didn't move.

"I read a book about a frog," Josefina said. "A bad witch made him into a frog, but he was a prince — "

CROAK! CROAK! CROAK! The big hat jumped on the bed.

"Shhh!" Josefina said. "This frog was a prince — "

CROAK! CROAK! CROAK! The hat jumped off the bed onto the mat.

Josefina took the hat off. Frog hopped up on the bed. His big, yellow eyes looked at Josefina. He didn't blink.

"Are you telling me something?" Josefina asked. "Are you telling me that you are a prince?"

CROAK! CROAK! CROAK! CROAK! CROAK! Frog jumped so high he almost bumped on the wall.

"Oh, be careful!" Josefina said. She stared at the frog. "In the book, the princess kissed him. That was when he turned back into a prince."

CROAK! said Frog. He sat very still.

"The Señora will like you if you're a prince," Josefina said. She bent over and kissed him quickly on his head. Frog's head was cold and wet and bumpy. Josefina sat back and looked at him.

"You're not a prince," she said. "You're still a frog."

CROAK! He sounded sad.

"And I'm not a princess. Sometimes mother calls me her little Princesita. But I'm not."

CROAK! said Frog.

Someone knocked on the door. Josefina put the hat over the frog, just in time.

It was the Señora. She came into the room, and so did Loco. "Who are you talking to, Josefina?" the Señora asked.

Loco jumped on the bed. He sniffed around the big hat.

The hat began to hop across the bed. Loco looked surprised. So did the Señora.

"What is it?" she asked. She picked up the hat.

Frog jumped on her back.

"Help! Help!" the Señora yelled. "What is it?"

Josefina had to laugh. The Señora looked so funny. "It's just a frog," she said.

The Señora's face was red. "I don't like frogs," she said. "Get it off!" Her voice was so loud that Loco hid under the bed. She shook herself. Frog fell on the mat.

Josefina picked him up. "What will I do with him?" she asked.

"I don't know. I don't care. Take him away. Take him away now!"

Josefina had never seen the Señora look so mean. "But city streets are not safe for frogs." Josefina felt like crying.

"Take him away *now*," the Señora said.

Josefina put the frog back in the bag. "I think he's a prince," she said.

CROAK! CROAK! CROAK! said the frog.

"Out!" said the Señora.

Josefina walked down the street. She stopped. "I know," she said. "I'll take you to the park. There is grass to hop on. There are bugs to eat. A city park will be safe for a frog."

There were lots of people in the park. A man stood on the grass. Boys and girls were around him.

"Frog! Look!" Josefina said.

Frog couldn't look. He was in the bag.

"All the boys and girls have frogs," Josefina said. "What are they doing?"

CROAK! said Frog. He didn't know. He couldn't see. He was in the bag.

"Frog!" Josefina said. "It's a frog jumping contest!"

"Number three is Hal of the Hill," the man on the grass called. A boy held up a big, green frog.

"Number four is Peg Legs," the man called. A girl held up a brown frog.

"We don't have number five," the man said. "Prince Croak A Lot got lost on the way here."

CROAK! CROAK! CROAK! CROAK! said the frog in the bag. He hopped so hard that Josefina dropped the bag.

A girl stood away from the other children. She looked sad. Her eyes were red from crying.

Josefina picked up the bag and ran toward the girl. "Look here!" she called. "I think I've found the prince."

Josefina gave the bag to the other child. She opened it and looked inside. Then she began to smile. She took the frog out of the bag. "Oh, thank you," she said. "Thank you for finding him."

CROAK! CROAK! said Prince Croak A Lot. CROAK! CROAK! CROAK!

Josefina smiled. "You didn't look like a prince," she said. "But now I understand. A prince can be as green as grass. A prince can have yellow eyes. A prince can be cold and bumpy. Who says he can't?"

Josefina looked across the park. She could see girls standing in line to read for the play. "Who says a princess has to have golden hair? Who says she has to have blue eyes?"

She patted Prince Croak A Lot's head. "Thank you," Josefina said softly.

"Thank you again for finding my frog," the girl said. "We have to hurry to be in the contest."

"I have to hurry too," Josefina said. She began to run. "Good luck in the contest, Prince," she called.

CROAK! CROAK! CROAK! said the prince.
Josefina smiled. Maybe that was frog talk.
Maybe that meant good luck to you too, Josefina.

Lights! Camera! Action! Croak!

With two or three classmates, choose a part of the story that you would like to act out in a puppet show. Then make puppets of the characters in that part of the story. Draw a picture of each character and paste it onto a popsicle stick. Each person in your group should have a puppet. When you know your parts and are ready, perform the scene using the puppets. On with the show!

Eve Bunting

Eve Bunting writes about **giants, zoos, dinosaurs, whales, wild horses, robots,** and children just like you. What keeps her going? "I like to write," *Bunting* says.

Here is another *Eve Bunting* book that you might enjoy reading: **The Mother's Day Mice.** The three mouse brothers find special ways to show their love for Mother on Mother's Day.

The Years of Growing Up

First haircut

First pet

First birthday

Playing in the park

age 5	age 6	age 7	age 8	?

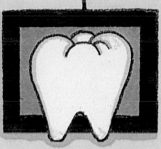

Losing a
first tooth

First big trip
away from home

First day of school

This time line shows some
special events that might
happen to someone like you.
You might want to make a
time line of your own life.
You can use it to show the
events that have made your
life special.

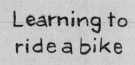

Learning to
ride a bike

49

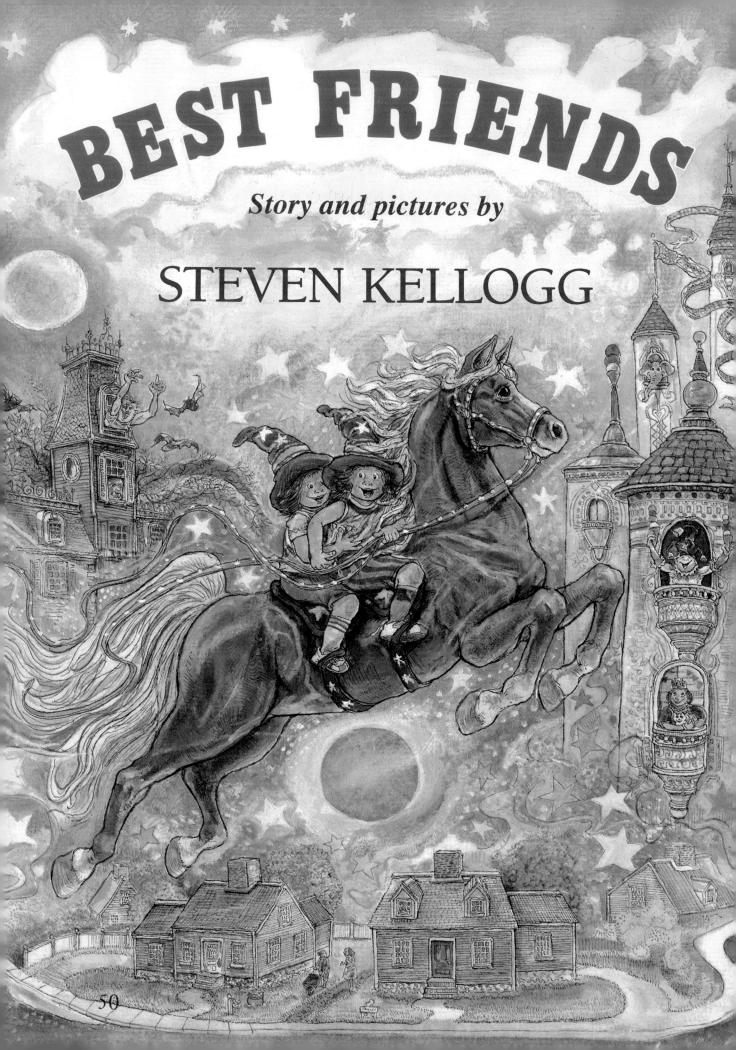

BEST FRIENDS

Story and pictures by

STEVEN KELLOGG

Louise Jenkins and I love horses, but we aren't allowed to have real ones.

I said, "Let's pretend that a stallion named Golden Silverwind lives in a stable between our houses." Louise loved the idea.

At school we pushed our desks together. And we played on the same team. At lunch we shared our chocolate milk. Chocolate is Louise's favorite, and it's mine too.

After school we pretended that we rode Golden Silverwind. Our magic witch hats gave us the power to make our neighborhood anything we wanted it to be.

And after dark, when it seemed to be haunted, we weren't scared as long as we were together. We were best friends.

Summer came, and so did Louise's aunt and uncle. They took her to a mountain resort for a vacation. Louise told me that she didn't want to go. "It will be awful," she said. "And I'll miss you every day."

When she left, our neighborhood turned into a lonely desert. If only Louise would be able to escape.

I even wished she'd get a contagious disease so they'd have to let her come home.

I wouldn't be afraid of catching it. I'd nurse her back to health with chocolate milk.

I missed her so much! I wished that Golden Silverwind and I could rescue her!

Finally I got a postcard. It said:

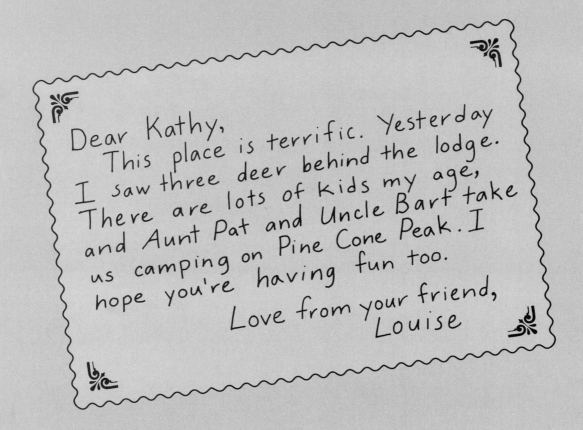

Dear Kathy,
This place is terrific. Yesterday I saw three deer behind the lodge. There are lots of kids my age, and Aunt Pat and Uncle Bart take us camping on Pine Cone Peak. I hope you're having fun too.
Love from your friend,
Louise

Later I heard Mrs. Jenkins say that Louise had made lots of new friends and was having the best summer of her life.

It wasn't fair. She wasn't lonely like me. She wasn't missing me at all.

Louise Jenkins was a traitor! She was my *worst* friend.

I wished that a volcanic eruption would blast Pine Cone Peak into pebbles.

Mom told me not to be jealous of Louise's new friends.

Later she said, "I heard that the house across the street has been sold. Maybe there'll be someone your age in the new family."

I prayed for fifty kids my age. Fifty new best friends with *real* horses!

When the moving man came, I asked him, "How many people in the new family?"

He said, "One."

I asked if it was someone my age.

He said, "Nope, it's Mr. Jode. He's seventy-two."

This was the worst summer of my life! The new family was one old man!

Mom said we should be good neighbors, and she sent me to invite Mr. Jode for a cookout.

When he saw my witch hat he said, "I wish you'd use your magic powers to help me find good homes for the new puppies that Sarah is expecting."

I ran home to ask Mom if I could have one. She said yes.

I couldn't wait to have a puppy of my own. And if Louise Jenkins wanted to play with it after she got back from Pine Cone Peak I'd say "NEVER!" That would fix her.

Mr. Jode and I talked about how much fun it would be when the puppies were born. I told him I wanted a spotted one just like Sarah.

"The first spotted one will be yours," he promised.

One day Mrs. Jenkins showed up and said, "I understand that your dog is expecting puppies. I'd like to reserve one for my daughter, Louise."

I couldn't stand to think of Louise having one of Sarah's puppies. I told Mr. Jode that I would keep all of them.

Mr. Jode said, "Three years ago Sarah had eight puppies in one litter. Would your mother want that many dogs?"

I had to admit that eight dogs would drive my mom crazy.

Mr. Jode asked me if I was afraid that Louise wouldn't give her puppy a good home. I had to admit that she would.

A week later Louise came back. Her mother had already told her that we were both getting puppies, and she was all excited about us raising them together.

Next she started talking about all the campouts on Pine Cone Peak, and how her uncle and aunt had already planned a return trip for the following summer.

I pretended to be very interested in my book.

Then she told me that she was glad to be home, and that she had missed me very much.

She had brought me a red Pine Cone Peak sweatshirt, a sparrow's feather, a rock collection, and a whistle on a lanyard that she had woven herself.

I told her how much I'd missed her. But I didn't tell her how mad I had been.

I took Louise to meet my new friends. I knew that they would all like each other, and they did. I said, "Aren't Sarah's spots beautiful? I'm going to get the first puppy that looks like her."

A few nights later Mr. Jode called to say that Sarah was having her puppies.

By the time we arrived, one puppy had already been born. It was brown. Mr. Jode handed him to Louise saying, "When he grows up, he'll look just like Sarah's mother."

Sarah went to sleep. Mr. Jode and Louise made hot chocolate and tried to think of a name for her puppy. I couldn't wait for mine to be born.

Sarah slept for hours. Finally Mr. Jode said, "It looks like there's only one puppy this time. Sarah has never had such a small litter before."

I felt awful.

It wasn't fair! Louise got to spend the whole summer camping on Pine Cone Peak, and now she had Sarah's only puppy.

Louise said, "I think the brown puppy should belong to both of us. We could name him Golden Silverwind."

Mr. Jode said, "I'll build him a dog house between your houses."

"And Sarah and I will help with his training."

When I got home, I kept thinking how lucky I was to have a special friend like Louise. I was already worried about how much I would miss her when she went away next summer.

But at least this time when she's camping on Pine Cone Peak I'll have Golden Silverwind all to myself.

THE END

Sharing Problems
What Would You Do?

Louise and Kathy solved their problem by building a dog house between their two yards.

With a partner, discuss how you might solve each of these problems.

1. Your two best friends invite you to their birthday parties. The parties are on the same day at the same time. What will you do?

2. Your best friend does not like your new friend. What will you do?

Steven Kellogg

Steven Kellogg loved making up stories for his little sisters. He would sit between his sisters and draw pictures to go with the stories as he told them. That is how *Kellogg* started his career as a writer and artist. Since then he has written and illustrated over **fifty books!**

Here are some other *Kellogg* books you might enjoy: **Can I Keep Him?** Arnold wants a pet, but his mother doesn't like cats, dogs, or tigers.

The Mysterious Tadpole
When a little tadpole gets too big for the bathtub, it's time for a clever solution.

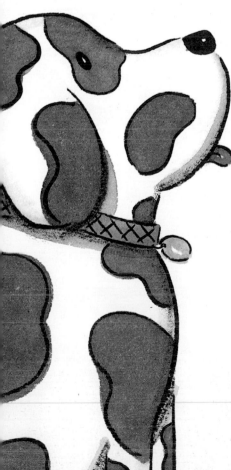

61

DID YOU KNOW

As you get older and grow up, your body grows up too! Here are some interesting facts about your body that will grow on you.

SKIN-TIGHT

Almost every four weeks, a new layer of skin replaces the old layer of skin.

WHAT A BRAIN!

Babies have brains that weigh about three ounces. Adults have brains that weigh about three pounds. That's sixteen times bigger!

MUSCLE-BOUND

When you smile you use fourteen muscles. Fingers have no muscles.

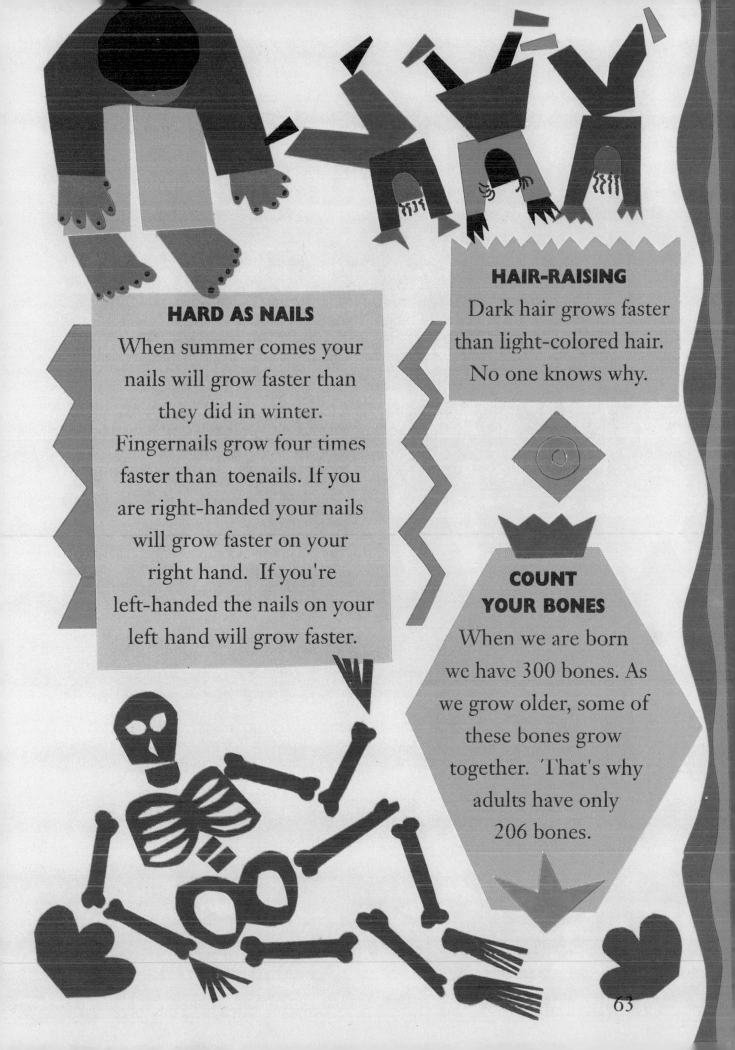

HARD AS NAILS

When summer comes your nails will grow faster than they did in winter. Fingernails grow four times faster than toenails. If you are right-handed your nails will grow faster on your right hand. If you're left-handed the nails on your left hand will grow faster.

HAIR-RAISING

Dark hair grows faster than light-colored hair. No one knows why.

COUNT YOUR BONES

When we are born we have 300 bones. As we grow older, some of these bones grow together. That's why adults have only 206 bones.

Ronald Morgan Goes to Bat

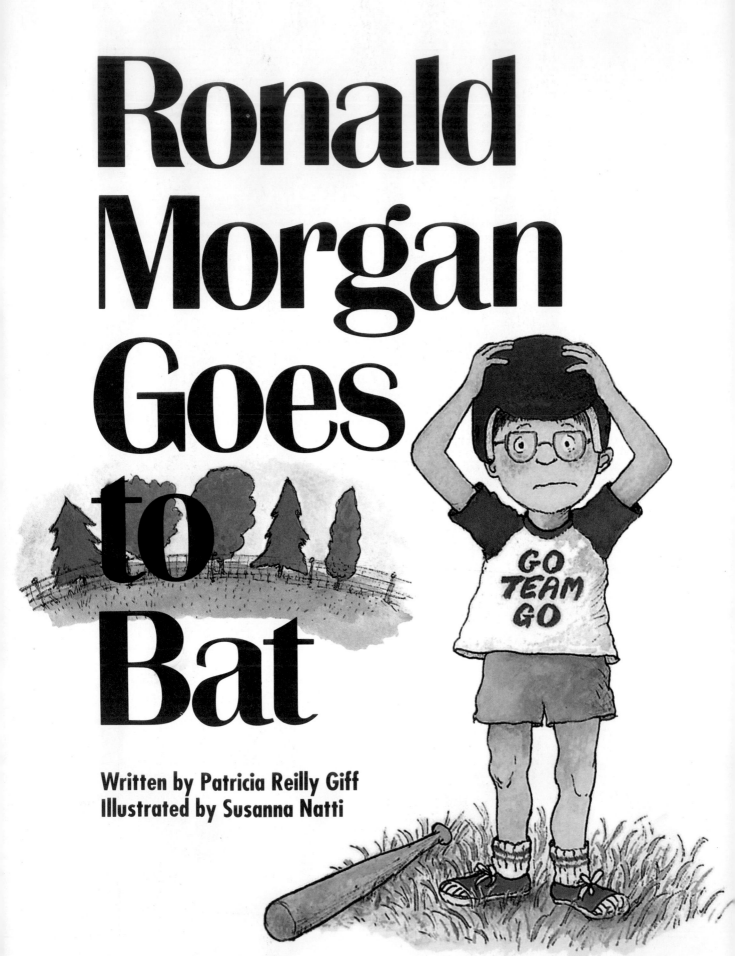

Written by Patricia Reilly Giff
Illustrated by Susanna Natti

Baseball started today. Mr. Spano said everyone could play.

"Even me?" I asked.

And Tom said, "You're letting Ronald Morgan play? He can't hit, he can't catch. He can't do anything."

Mr. Spano looked at me. "Everyone," he said.

"Yahoo!" I yelled.

I pulled on my red and white shirt, the one that says GO TEAM GO, and ran outside to the field.

"Two things," Mr. Spano told us. "Try hard, and keep your eye on the ball."

Then it was time to practice. Michael was up first. He smacked the ball with the bat. The ball flew across the field.

"Good," said Mr. Spano.

"Great, Slugger!" I yelled. "We'll win every game."

It was my turn next. I put on the helmet, and stood at home plate.

"Ronald Morgan," said Rosemary. "You're holding the wrong end of the bat."

Quickly I turned it around. I clutched it close to the end.

Whoosh went the first ball.

Whoosh went the second one.

Wham went the third. It hit me in the knee.

"Are you all right?" asked Michael.

But I heard Tom say, "I knew it. Ronald Morgan's the worst."

At snack time, we told Miss Tyler about the team.

"I don't hit very well," I said.

And Rosemary said, "The ball hits him instead."

Everybody laughed, even me.

I shook my head. "I hope it doesn't happen again."

Miss Tyler gave me some raisins. "You
have to hit the ball before it hits you,"
she said.

We played every day. I tried hard, but
the ball came fast. I closed my eyes and
swung.

"If only he could hit the ball once,"
Rosemary said. And Billy shook his head.
I couldn't tell them I was afraid of the ball.

"Go team go," I whispered.

One day, the team sat on the grass. We
watched the third grade play. They were big,
they were strong, they were good. Johnny
hit a home run, and Joy tagged a man out.

"We'll never hit like that," said Tom.

And Rosemary said, "We'll never catch
like that either."

But I said, "Our team is the best."

Mr. Spano nodded. "That's the spirit,
Ronald."

Mr. Spano told us, "Now we'll run the bases. Rosemary, you can go first."

Rosemary went fast. She raced for first base.

"Terrific, Speedy!" I yelled.

"Let me go next," I said. "I can do that, too."

But the field was muddy. My sneaker came off.

Jimmy said, "That kid's running bases the wrong way."

And Tom yelled, "Ronald Morgan. You're heading for third base."

The next day, we worked on catching.
I was out in left field. While I waited, I
found a stick, and started to scratch out the
mud. I wrote G for go. I wrote G for
great. Our team is the best, I thought.
Then I wrote H for hit. H for home run.
If only I could do that.

Just then I heard yelling. Someone had
hit the ball. "Catch it, Ronald!" Tom
shouted.

I put down the stick. I put up my mitt.
Too late. The ball sailed into the trees.

Mr. Spano took us for ice cream. "You deserve it for trying," he said. "Our team is really good."

I had a chocolate cone. Michael's a slugger, I thought. And Rosemary can really run. But I'm still afraid of the ball.

On the way home, we saw some kids playing ball. "Want to hit a few?" Michael asked.

I shook my head. "Maybe I won't play ball anymore."

Michael said, "We need you. You have spirit. You help the team feel good."

"But how can we win?" I asked. "I can't even hit the ball."

I saw my father and ran to catch up. "See you, Michael," I said.

My father asked, "How's the champ?"

"I'm the worst," I said.

"I was the worst, too," said my father. "But then . . ."

"What?"

My father laughed. "I stopped closing my eyes when I swung."

"Maybe that's what I do."

"How about a little practice?" he asked.

We went into the yard. My father threw me some balls. I missed the first one . . . I missed the second. And then . . .

I opened my eyes and swung. *Crack* went the ball. "Ouch!" went my father. "You hit me in the knee."

"Home run!" yelled my mother.

"Sorry," I said. "Hey, I did it!"

My father rubbed his knee. "You certainly did," he said.

I ran to pick up the ball. "See you later," I said.

My father smiled. "Where are you going?"

I grabbed the bat. "Some kids are playing ball. I think I'll hit a few."

I looked back. "And you know what else? I guess I'll stay on the team. I have spirit . . . and sometimes I can hit the ball. Mike was right. I think they need me."

Three Cheers for the Home Team!

Ronald Morgan was not the best baseball
player, but he had a lot of team spirit.
He always cheered for his team.
Make up a cheer for Ronald's team.
You may want to make it rhyme like this one.

**COME ON, ROSEMARY, RUN, RUN, RUN!
ONE MORE BASE AND THE GAME IS DONE!**

Now choose a partner, and act out your
cheer. Act it out with a lot of team spirit!

Patricia Reilly Giff

Patricia Reilly Giff has always loved reading. "I spent most of my childhood with a book in my hands," she said. "After school, I'd sit in the kitchen leaning against the warm radiator, **dreaming** over a story." *Giff* likes to write about her childhood and the things that interest her own children. Since 1979 she has written over fifteen books, some of them about Ronald Morgan.

Here is another Ronald Morgan book you may enjoy reading: **Watch Out, Ronald Morgan.** Things keep happening to Ronald Morgan. Does he need glasses?

A Year Later

Last summer I couldn't swim at all;
I couldn't even float!
I had to use a rubber tube
Or hang on to a boat;
I had to sit on shore
While everybody swam.
But now it's this summer
And I can!

Mary Ann Hoberman

GROW WITH THESE BOOKS!

Molly and the Slow Teeth
by Pat Ross
pictures by Jerry Milord

LIONEL AT LARGE
by Stephen Krensky
pictures by Susanna Natti

Eleanor Coerr
The Josefina Story Quilt
Pictures by Bruce Degen

Molly and the Slow Teeth
by Pat Ross
Molly thinks she'll never lose her baby teeth, so she tries to fool the tooth fairy.

Lionel at Large
by Stephen Krensky
Lionel has big problems. Will he ever learn to like beans or get used to his sister's snake?

The Josefina Story Quilt
by Eleanor Coerr
When her family goes to California in a covered wagon, Faith takes along her pet hen, Josefina.

The New Girl At School
by Judy Delton
Being in a new school isn't much fun at first, but Marcia learns to make new friends.

The Half-Birthday Party
by Charlotte Pomerantz
Daniel plans his sister's half-birthday party, but forgets something important.

BOOK 2

TOMIE dePAOLA

Tomie dePaola

Some people write wonderful stories. Other people draw great pictures. Tomie dePaola does both. In this book you will read three of the many stories he has written and illustrated. One of the stories is funny, one is serious, and one is almost true. After each story, you will also read a special message that Tomie dePaola wrote just for you.

Table of Contents

The Art Lesson

written and illustrated by Tomie dePaola

Tommy knew he wanted to be an artist when he grew up. He drew pictures everywhere he went. It was his favorite thing to do.

His friends had favorite things to do, too. Jack collected all kinds of turtles. Herbie made huge cities in his sandbox. Jeannie, Tommy's best friend, could do cartwheels and stand on her head.

But Tommy drew
and drew and drew.
His twin cousins,
who were already grown
up, were in art school

learning to be real artists. They told him not to copy
and to practice, practice, practice. So, he did.

Tommy put his pictures up on the walls of his half of the bedroom.

His mom put them up all around the house.

His dad took them to the barber shop where he worked.

Tom and Nana, Tommy's Irish grandfather and grandmother, had his pictures in their grocery store.

Nana-Fall-River, his Italian grandmother, put one in a special frame on the table next to the photograph of Aunt Clo in her wedding dress.

Once Tommy took a flashlight and a pencil under the covers and drew pictures on his sheets. But when his mom changed the sheets on Monday and found them, she said, "No more drawing on the sheets, Tommy."

His mom and dad were having a new house built, so Tommy drew pictures of what it would look like when it was finished.

When the walls were up, one of the carpenters gave Tommy a piece of bright blue chalk.

Tommy took the chalk and drew beautiful pictures all over the unfinished walls.

But, when the painters came, his dad said, "That's it, Tommy. No more drawing on the walls."

Tommy couldn't wait to go to kindergarten. His brother, Joe, told him there was a real art teacher who came to the school to give ART LESSONS!

"When do we have our art lessons?" Tommy asked the kindergarten teacher.

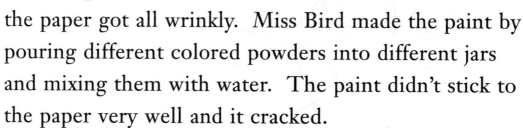

"Oh, you won't have your art lessons until next year," said Miss Bird. "But, we *are* going to paint pictures tomorrow."

It wasn't much fun.

The paint was awful and the paper got all wrinkly. Miss Bird made the paint by pouring different colored powders into different jars and mixing them with water. The paint didn't stick to the paper very well and it cracked.

If it was windy when Tommy carried his picture home, the paint blew right off the paper.

"At least you get more than one piece of paper in kindergarten," his brother, Joe, said. "When the art teacher comes, you only get one piece."

Tommy knew that the art teacher came to the school every other Wednesday. He could tell she was an artist because she wore a blue smock over her dress and she always carried a big box of thick colored chalks.

Once, Tommy and Jeannie looked at the drawings that were hung up in the hallway. They were done by the first graders.

"Your pictures are much better," Jeannie told Tommy. "Next year when we have real art lessons, you'll be the best one!"

Tommy could hardly wait. He practiced all summer.
Then, on his birthday, which was right after school
began, his mom and dad gave him a box of sixty-four
Crayola crayons. Regular boxes of crayons had red,
orange, yellow, green, blue, violet, brown and black. This
box had so many other colors: blue-violet, turquoise,
red-orange, pink and even gold, silver and copper.

"Class," said Miss Landers, the first-grade teacher, "next month, the art teacher will come to our room, so on Monday instead of Singing, we will practice using our crayons."

On Monday, Tommy brought his sixty-four crayons to school. Miss Landers was not pleased.

"Everyone must use the same crayons," she said. "SCHOOL CRAYONS!"

School crayons had only the same old eight colors.

As Miss Landers passed them out to the class, she said, "These crayons are school property, so do not break them, peel off the paper, or wear down the points."

"How am I supposed to practice being an artist with SCHOOL CRAYONS?" Tommy asked Jack and Herbie.

"That's enough, Tommy," Miss Landers said. "And I want you to take those birthday crayons home with you and leave them there."

And Joe was right.
They only got ONE
piece of paper.

Finally, the day
of the art lesson came.
Tommy could hardly
sleep that night.

The next morning, he hid the box of sixty-four
crayons under his sweater and went off to school.
He was ready!

The classroom door opened and in walked the art
teacher. Miss Landers said, "Class, this is Mrs. Bowers,
the art teacher. Patty, who is our paper monitor this
week, will give out one piece of paper to each of you.
And remember, don't ruin it because it is the only piece
you'll get. Now, pay attention to Mrs. Bowers."

"Class," Mrs. Bowers began, "because Thanksgiving is not too far away, we will learn to draw a Pilgrim man, a Pilgrim woman and a turkey. Watch carefully and copy me."

Copy? COPY? Tommy knew that *real* artists didn't copy. This was terrible. This was supposed to be a real art lesson. He folded his arms and just sat there.

"Now what's the matter?" Miss Landers asked. Tommy looked past her and spoke right to Mrs. Bowers.

"I'm going to be an artist when I grow up and my cousins told me that real artists don't copy. And besides, Miss Landers won't let me use my own sixty-four Crayola crayons."

"Well, well," Mrs. Bowers said. "What are we going to do?" She turned to Miss Landers and they whispered together. Miss Landers nodded.

"Now, Tommy," Mrs. Bowers said. "It wouldn't be fair to let you do something different from the rest of the class.

"But, I have an idea. If you draw the Pilgrim man and woman and the turkey, and if there's any time left, I'll give you *another* piece of paper and you can do your own picture with your own crayons. Can you do that?"

"I'll try," Tommy said, with a big smile.

And he did.

And he did.

And he still does.

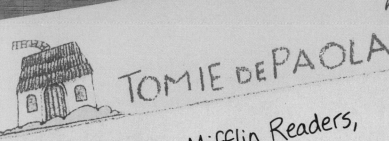

Dear Houghton Mifflin Readers,

Did you know that when I was only four years old, I knew that I wanted to be an artist when I grew up? So, I decided to write the story about my wanting to be an artist. It was fun telling all the things that really happened, but I made up some things, too. I made up some of the teachers' names. I made up that it happened in first grade. It really happened in second grade. But, I really did have sixty-four Crayola crayons. I really did have to draw a Pilgrim man, a Pilgrim woman, and a turkey! And I did draw pictures on my sheets!

When I grow up...

When he was young, Tomie dePaola liked to draw pictures. When he grew up, he became an artist.

What do YOU like to do? Make a list of four things you like to do now. Choose one thing on your list that you could do as a job when you grow up. Then draw a picture of yourself doing that job.

Now One Foot, Now the Other

written and illustrated by Tomie dePaola

Bobby was named after his best friend, his grandfather, Bob. When Bobby was just a baby, his grandfather told everyone, "Bobby will be three years old before he can say Grandpa, so I'm going to have him call me Bob."

And "Bob" was the first word Bobby said.

Bob was the one who helped Bobby learn to walk.

"Hold on to my hands, Bobby," his grandfather said. "Now one foot, now the other."

One of the best things Bob and Bobby did was to play with the old wooden blocks that were kept on a shelf, in the small sewing room under the front stairs.

The blocks had letters on two sides, numbers on two sides and pictures of animals and other things on the last two sides. Bob and Bobby would slowly, very slowly put the blocks one on top of the other, building a tall tower. There were thirty blocks.

Sometimes the tower would fall down when only half the blocks were piled up.

Sometimes the tower would be almost finished.

"Just one more block," Bob would say.

"And that's the elephant block," Bobby would say.

And they would carefully put the elephant block on the very top.

But Bob would sneeze and the tower would fall down. Bobby would laugh and laugh.

"Elephants always make you sneeze, Bob," Bobby would say.

"We'll just have to try the next time," his grandfather would say.

Then Bob would sit Bobby on his knee and tell him stories.

"Bob, tell me the story about how you taught me to walk," Bobby would say.

And his grandfather would tell Bobby how he held Bobby's hands and said, "Now one foot, now the other. And before you knew it . . ."

On Bobby's fifth birthday, Bob and he had a special day. They went to the amusement park. They rode a roller coaster, ate hot dogs and ice cream. They had their pictures taken in a machine, and they sang a song and made a phonograph record. And when it got dark, they watched the fireworks.

On the way home, Bob told Bobby stories.

"Now, tell me the story about how you taught me to walk," Bobby said.

And Bob did.

Not long after Bobby's birthday, his grandfather got very sick. Bobby came home and his grandfather wasn't there.

"Bob is in the hospital," Dad told Bobby. "He's had what is called a *stroke*."

"I want to go see him," Bobby said.

"You can't, honey," Mom told him. "Right now Bob's too sick to see anyone. He can't move his arms and legs, and he can't talk. The doctor's not sure if he knows who anyone is. We'll just have to wait and hope Bob gets better."

Bobby didn't know what to do. He didn't want to eat; he had a hard time going to sleep at night. Bob just *had* to get better.

Months and months and months went by. Bob was still in the hospital. Bobby missed his grandfather.

One day when Bobby came home from school, his father told him that Bob was coming home.

"Now, Bobby," Dad said, "Bob is still very sick. He can't move or talk. When he sees your mother and me, he still doesn't know who we are, and the doctor doesn't think he'll get any better. So, don't be scared if he doesn't remember you."

But Bobby *was* scared. His grandfather *didn't* remember him. He just lay in bed. And when Dad carried him, Bob sat in a chair. But he didn't talk or even move.

One day, Bob tried to say something to Bobby, but the sound that came out was awful. Bobby ran out of the room.

"Bob sounded like a monster!" Bobby cried.

"He can't help it, Bobby," Mom said.

So, Bobby went back to the room where Bob was sitting. It looked like a tear was coming down Bob's face.

"I didn't mean to run away, Bob. I was scared. I'm sorry," Bobby said. "Do you know who I am?"

Bobby thought he saw Bob blink his eye.

"Mom, Mom," Bobby called. "Bob knows who I am."

"Oh, Bobby," Mom said. "You're just going to upset yourself. Your grandfather doesn't recognize any of us."

But Bobby knew better. He ran to the small
sewing room, under the front stairs. He took the
blocks off the shelf and
ran back to where Bob
was sitting.

Bob's mouth made
a small smile.

Bobby began to
build the tower.

Halfway . . .
Almost to the top . . .
Only one block left.

"OK, Bob," said Bobby.
"Now the elephant block."
And Bob made a strange
noise that sounded like a
sneeze.

The blocks fell down
and Bob smiled and moved
his fingers up and down.

Bobby laughed and
laughed. Now he knew
that Bob would get better.

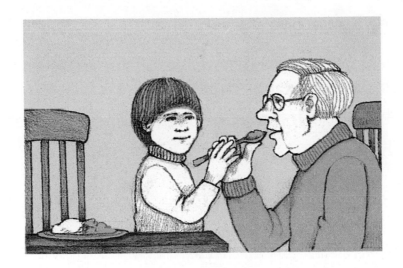

And Bob did. Slowly, he began to talk a little. It sounded strange but he could say "Bobby" just as clear as day. Bob began to move his fingers and then his hands. Bobby still helped to feed his grandfather, but one day Bob could almost hold a spoon by himself. But, he still couldn't walk.

When the weather got nice and warm, Dad carried Bob out to a chair set up on the lawn. Bobby sat with him.

"Bobby," Bob said. "Story." So, Bobby told Bob some stories.

Then, Bob stood up very slowly.

"You. Me. Walk," said Bob.

Bobby knew exactly what Bob wanted to do.

Bobby stood in front of Bob and let Bob lean on his shoulders.

"OK, Bob. Now one foot."

Bob moved one foot.

"Now the other foot."

Bob moved the other.

By the end of the summer, Bob and Bobby could walk to the end of the lawn and Bob could talk better and better each day.

On Bobby's sixth birthday, Bobby got the
blocks. Slowly he built up the tower. Only one
block to go.

"Here, elephant block," Bob said.

Bobby put it on top.

Bob sneezed!

"Elephants always
make you sneeze, Bob,"
Bobby said. "We'll just
have to try the next time.
Now, tell me some stories."

Bob did.

Then Bob said, "Bobby, tell story how you teach
Bob to walk."

"Well, Bob, you leaned on my shoulders and then I
said, 'Now one foot, now the other.' And before you
knew it . . ."

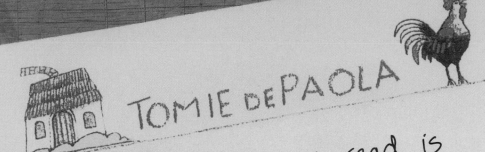

TOMIE dePAOLA

The story you just read is based on something that really happened. My grandfather, Tom, had a stroke just like Bob in the story. I was a grown-up though, and my grandfather didn't get better. But the part about the blocks is real. If you came to visit me, you'd see them on a shelf in my living room.

Something Special

Bob and Bobby shared lots of special times together. They built towers with blocks, told stories, and spent a special day at the amusement park.

Think of a special time you have shared with someone in your family. Tell a story about this time to a classmate.

Strega Nona's
Magic Lessons

STORY AND PICTURES BY

Tomie de Paola

ambolona, the baker's daughter, was angry. Every day, summer, fall, winter, and spring, she had to get up before the sun to bake the bread. Then, piling the loaves on her head, she went to deliver them. But her work wasn't finished. Rushing back to the bakery, she had to mix the flour and salt and water and yeast and set the dough to rise for tomorrow's bread.

"Don't forget," her father, the baker, would say, "to make the cookies and bake the cakes. And remember, Bambolona, to clean up everything spic and span! I'm going now to see my friends." And off he would go to sit all day in the square of the little town in Calabria.

One day Bambolona said, "Papa, there is too much work to do. I need some help."

"Get up earlier," her father said.

"But I get up now before the sun!" said Bambolona. "And I'm the last one in town to get to bed."

"That's the way things are," her father said as he went out the door on his way to the square. "And don't forget," he called back, "you have a wedding cake to bake."

That did it. Bambolona dusted the flour from her hands and took off her apron. "I'm going to *change* the way things are," she said. "I'll go see Strega Nona. She's so wise, she'll help me."

"I think I know how to help you," Strega Nona said after hearing Bambolona's sad tale. "So many people come to me with their troubles. I could certainly use some help. Why not stay with me and I will teach you my magic."

"Oh, Strega Nona," said Bambolona, "thank you!"

"We'll start today," said Strega Nona.

Now, Big Anthony, who worked around the house and in the garden for Strega Nona, was listening. He was always listening to what other people were talking about instead of working. "Strega Nona!" he shouted, running into the house. "Me too! Teach me your magic too!"

"Oh, Anthony," Strega Nona said with a smile, "I can't do that. Why don't you go and milk the goat." Now Big Anthony was the one who was angry!

"I'll show
Strega Nona,"
he muttered.
"I'll just go and
work for the
baker, now that

Bambolona has left." Down the hill Big Anthony ran.

The baker hired him on the spot. "The first thing
you do is mix the dough," the baker told Big Anthony.
"Put in this much flour, this much salt, this much
water, and this much yeast." He looked hard at Big
Anthony's smiling face.

"Do you understand? *The yeast makes the dough rise.* Now mix it right away, and by the time I get back at six o'clock, the dough will be ready to make into loaves."

"*Sì Signore* — yes sir!" Big Anthony said.

The baker walked out the door and toward the square.

"I'll just look at everything first," said Big Anthony, poking around.

"Cookies!" He ate one, then another. "Cakes!" He ate one, then another. Big Anthony ate them all. In fact, he was still eating when the clock in the square struck four.

"*Mamma mia!*" said Big Anthony. "I forgot to mix the dough. It won't rise in time. Ah! I know. *The yeast makes the dough rise!* I'll just put in a lot more of that, and the dough will rise much faster!"

"I'll still have time for a nap," he said when he got through. He sat down and promptly fell asleep.

What a sight the baker saw when he returned.

"OUT!" shouted the baker.

"What's the matter, Big Anthony?" asked
Signora Rosa.

"The baker threw me out. Now I have no job," he
answered. "And it's Strega Nona's fault. I never would
have left her house if she had let me learn to be a
Strega."

"Silly goose," said Signora Rosa. "Whoever heard
of a man being a *Strega*?"

126

All of a sudden Big Anthony's eyes lit up, and off he ran.

"To cure a headache, you must first fill the bowl with water," Strega Nona was telling Bambolona. "Next you add a few drops of olive oil. Then you say these magic words . . ."

Knock, knock, knock. Strega Nona went to the door.

"Oh, Strega Nona," said a tall girl, standing there.
"All my life I've wanted to learn your magic. Will you
teach me? Please?"

Santo Cielo — dear me," said Strega Nona. "What
is your name, my girl?"

"Uh-h-h — Antonia," said the girl.

"Why do you want to learn my magic, Antonia?" Strega Nona asked.

"Oh, so that I can help people," said Antonia. "Ever since I was a little girl, I've wanted to become a *Strega*."

"Ah, in that case," said Strega Nona, "come right in. This is Bambolona. She is learning my magic, too."

Bambolona stared at Antonia and then at Strega Nona.

"How nice. Two girls to teach," Strega Nona said. She smiled at Bambolona and then she began. "To learn magic and practice it well," she said, "you must learn to see *and* not to see. You must learn to remember *and* to forget; to be still *and* to be busy. But, mostly you must be faithful to your work. Do you understand, my dears?"

"*Sì* — yes, Strega Nona," said Bambolona.

"No — *no,*" said Antonia. "When are we going to learn how to do the *magic* things?"

"In time," said Strega Nona. "Now let's practice some of the magic words. Repeat in the right order after me."

Soon Bambolona said all of them by heart. Antonia kept mixing them up.

Bambolona learned the cure for headaches.
Antonia didn't.

Bambolona learned to make love potions.
Antonia didn't.

Bambolona learned how to get rid of warts.
Antonia didn't.

"Bambolona," said Strega Nona, "I think you are ready now to learn more powerful magic. This is a special book. It is very ancient and contains many magic secrets. Tomorrow we will begin with it."

"Oh *Grazie,* Strega Nona," said Bambolona.

"Me too, Strega Nona?" asked Antonia.

"Not yet, Antonia," said Strega Nona. "You have other things to learn."

That night while everyone slept, Antonia crept into Strega Nona's house. "Bambolona thinks she's so smart," said Antonia. "I'll just read that book tonight, and tomorrow I'll surprise her *and* Strega Nona."

The next morning Antonia was looking very tired. "Antonia," said Strega Nona, "watch and listen. Come, Bambolona. We will start."

"Wait — wait," shouted Antonia. "I have a surprise. I know some *real* magic. Watch me turn that iron kettle into a golden one."

"Are you sure, Antonia?" said Strega Nona, frowning.

"Yes, oh yes," said Antonia, beginning to mutter some strange-sounding words. But she stopped. "Wait! I remember now." She began again.

"Be careful, Antonia," warned Bambolona. "Magic can't be fooled with."

"I've got it now," Antonia said.

She muttered more words. Suddenly there was a bright flash, some smelly smoke, and the iron kettle . . . was still *there*!

But Strega Nona wasn't. Instead, where Strega Nona had been standing was a nice fat TOAD.

"Now see what you've done!" cried Bambolona.

"Oh *no!*" shouted Antonia. "Oh help! Help, somebody! Save Strega Nona! What have I done?"

"Strega Nona warned you to be careful with magic.

Now she's gone forever," Bambolona said.

"Strega Nona," wept Antonia, picking up the toad, "forgive me, forgive me. Please, Bambolona, you're so clever, you're so smart, please change her back again! I promise I'll never play with magic again . . ."

"I can't change that toad into Strega Nona," said Bambolona. "But I *can* change Antonia into . . . Big Anthony!" Bambolona pulled off Antonia's kerchief and — sure enough — there was Big Anthony!

"Oh, I'll never learn," howled Big Anthony, "I'll never learn. Oh, Strega Nona — Strega Nona — what have I done to you?"

"Perhaps," said Bambolona, "if you really promise to never, ever play with magic again, that will bring Strega Nona back."

"Do you really think that would work?" said Big Anthony, sobbing.

"It's worth a try," said Bambolona.

Big Anthony put down the toad. He closed his eyes tight and put his hand over his heart. "I promise, I *really* promise, that as long as I live I will never play with magic again. Just please bring Strega Nona back."

There was another bright
flash, some smelly smoke, and
presto! Strega Nona was back!

"Where am I?" said Strega
Nona. "Oh, I'm in my little
house. Whatever happened to
me? Hello, Bambolona. And,
why, Big Anthony, what are *you*
doing here? Where's sweet Antonia?"

"Tell her, Big Anthony," said Bambolona.

"Oh, Strega Nona," said Big Anthony, falling on his knees. He told Strega Nona what he had done. He was so busy crying and talking, he didn't see the nice fat toad hopping past him out the door.

"And so, Strega Nona, please," he said, "if you take me back, I promise to be good. I'll do all my chores and never play with magic again."

"All right, Anthony," said Strega Nona, smiling. "But before you go back to work, change your clothes. You're wearing Signora Rosa's nicest dress."

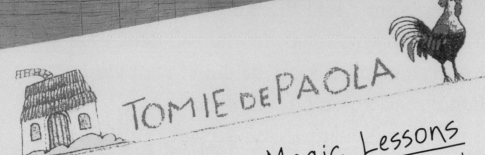

TOMIE dePAOLA

<u>Strega Nona's Magic Lessons</u> is a made-up story. I'm so glad I thought up Strega Nona, Big Anthony, and Bambolona. Strega Nona is a little bit like my Italian grandmother, and Big Anthony is like one of my cousins. I guess I don't know anyone like Bambolona. I love these characters and I hope you do, too. There are now four books about Strega Nona and probably more to come.

Now What?

At the end of the story, Big Anthony promises Strega Nona that he'll NEVER play with magic again. But will he keep his promise?

Think about what might happen after Big Anthony makes his promise. Then, with a partner, play the roles of Big Anthony and Strega Nona. Act out what they might do and say next.

Here's a poem by Tomie dePaola.

He drew the picture too.

The Secret Place

It was my secret place —
    down at the foot
    of my bed —
    under the covers.

It was very white.

I went there
    with a book, a flashlight,
    and the special pencil
    that my grandfather gave me.

To read —
    and to draw pictures
    on all that white.

It was my secret place
    for about a week —

Until my mother came
    to change the sheets.

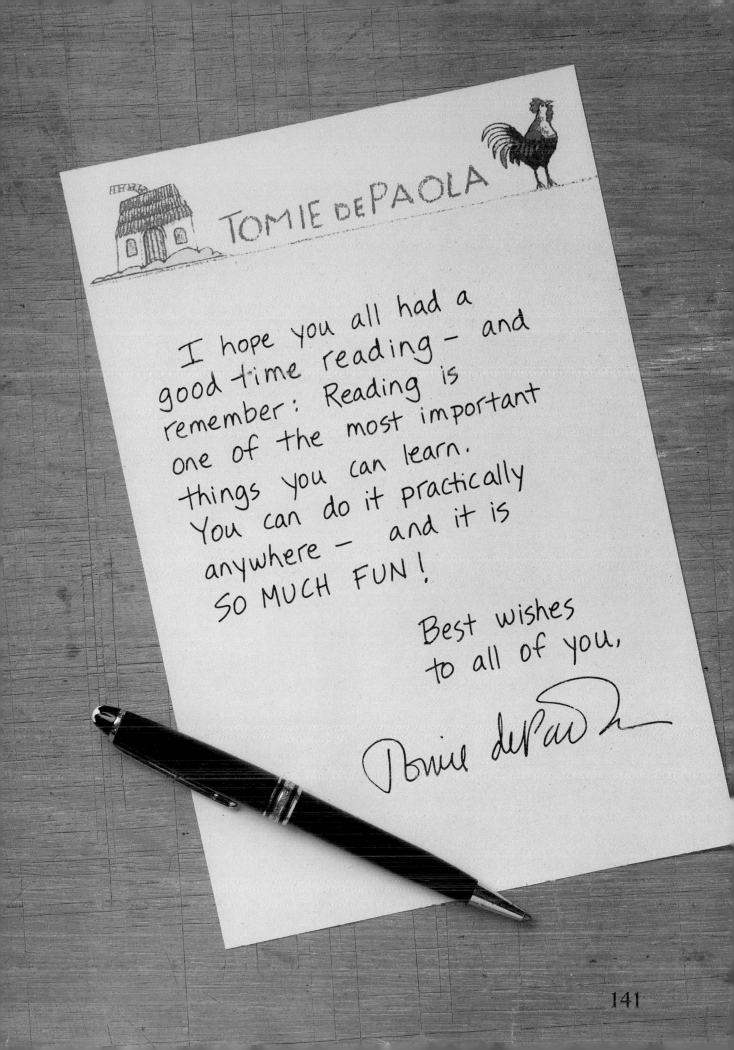

I hope you all had a good time reading — and remember: Reading is one of the most important things you can learn. You can do it practically anywhere — and it is SO MUCH FUN!

Best wishes to all of you,

Tomie dePaola

Picture yourself reading these books.

Like Tomie dePaola, other authors both write and illustrate their books. Here is another Tomie dePaola book, plus books by two other authors who illustrate their own books.

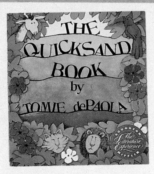

The Quicksand Book
by Tomie dePaola

What is quicksand? Where is it found? This funny book will answer your questions about quicksand.

Wings: A Tale of Two Chickens
by James Marshall

Poor Winnie the chicken may end up in a sly fox's dinner pot. Can Winnie's friend Harriet save her?

*George and Martha
Round and Round*
by James Marshall

George and Martha
are two hippos who
are friends forever
in these five funny
stories.

A Treeful of Pigs
by Arnold Lobel

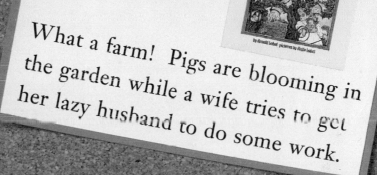

What a farm! Pigs are blooming in
the garden while a wife tries to get
her lazy husband to do some work.

*Frog and Toad
Together*
by Arnold Lobel

In these five stories,
Frog and Toad
learn that it is easy
being brave with a
friend.

BOOK 3

Aesop's Fables

Long, long ago a man named Aesop told
stories called fables. Through these stories,
Aesop tried to teach lessons, or morals, about
how people should live.

People enjoyed Aesop's fables so much
that they told them over and over again, in
many different ways.

Now, from Aesop to you, here are some
stories from long ago.

Table of Contents

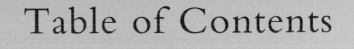

147

The Tortoise and the Hare

Janet Stevens

Once upon a time, there was a tortoise and a hare.

Tortoise was friendly and quiet. He did everything slowly. Hare was flashy and rude. He did everything quickly.

Hare liked to tease Tortoise about being so slow.

When Tortoise ate breakfast, Hare said, "By the time you finish your last bite, it will be dinnertime."

When Tortoise worked in his garden,
Hare said, "By the time you pick those spring
flowers, it will be winter."

One afternoon, Hare followed Tortoise to
the store. Hare teased him on the way. "By
the time you get there, the store will be
closed," he said. "You're so slow, I could
beat you at a race, hopping backwards on
one paw."

"But I could never beat you, Hare," said Tortoise.

"Yes, you could," said Tortoise's friends. "All you need is a little help."

"Then you *will* race me, Tortoise?" asked Hare.

Tortoise pulled his head into his shell.

"I don't want to," he said.

"You've got to," said his friends. "You've put up with that nasty hare long enough. We think you can win."

Tortoise didn't want to disappoint his friends, so he finally agreed to race against Hare.

Tortoise only had two-and-a-half weeks to get in shape before the big race. Rooster helped him out at the gym. Raccoon cooked him healthy meals. Frog went jogging with him every morning. By the day of the race, Tortoise was ready.

Animals from all over the county came to watch the tortoise and the hare.

Rooster read aloud the rules and described the course.

"Attention, everyone. The race will begin
when I sound this gong. The six-mile course
is marked by red flags. The first one to reach
the finish line wins. Runners, take your mark,
get set, GO!!" Raccoon sounded the gong.

Hare bolted out of sight before Tortoise
had taken his first step. The crowd roared
and cheered as Tortoise inched forward.

Hare was so far ahead that he decided to stop at Bear's house for something cool to drink.

Hare rested and sipped lemonade. Bear noticed something moving outside the window. "Hare, there goes Tortoise."

"What?" yelled Hare, running out the door.

Hare passed Tortoise for the second time. Then he decided to stop at Mouse's house for a snack.

As Hare munched on crackers and cheese, Mouse yelled, "Is that Tortoise I see out the window?"

"I'm not worried about that slowpoke," said Hare. "I've passed him twice already." Then he finished his snack and hopped out the door.

Hare passed Tortoise for a third time. Now, he was far ahead. He saw a pond and decided to stop and rest. The snacks had made him sleepy.

Hare was so sure that he would win, he took a nap in the soft grass. As he closed his eyes, he dreamed of victory.

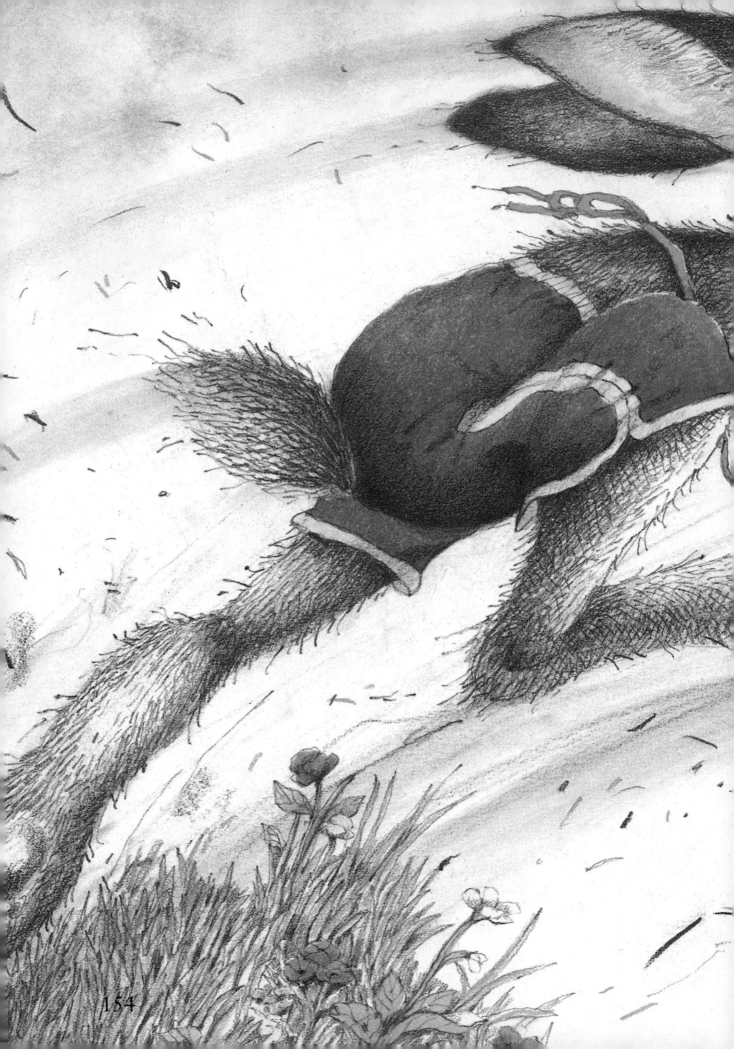

Suddenly, Hare woke up because the crowd was cheering.

"Yay, Tortoise," the crowd roared.

Tortoise was two steps away from the finish line.

"Slow down, you bowlegged reptile," screamed Hare as he tried to catch up.

But it was too late. Tortoise crossed the line just before the tornado of dust and fur that was Hare flew by. Tortoise had won the race. Hare couldn't believe it. That measly shell on legs had beaten him.

Tortoise smiled as his friends carried him on their shoulders. He had learned an important lesson:

HARD WORK AND PERSEVERANCE BRING REWARD.

TORTOISE

On Your Mark...

With a partner, make a map of the racecourse. Draw it on a piece of cardboard or paper. Show the places where Hare stopped. Then make cardboard figures of Tortoise and Hare. Use them to act out the story for your class.

VS HARE

Meet the Author

Janet Stevens is an author and an illustrator. When she met Tomie dePaola in 1978, he encouraged her to turn a popular children's song into a book. So she created *Animal Fair,* which was her first picture book.

Since then, Stevens has illustrated over ten books. She has retold and illustrated stories by Aesop and Mother Goose. You may enjoy reading her retelling of *Androcles and the Lion.*

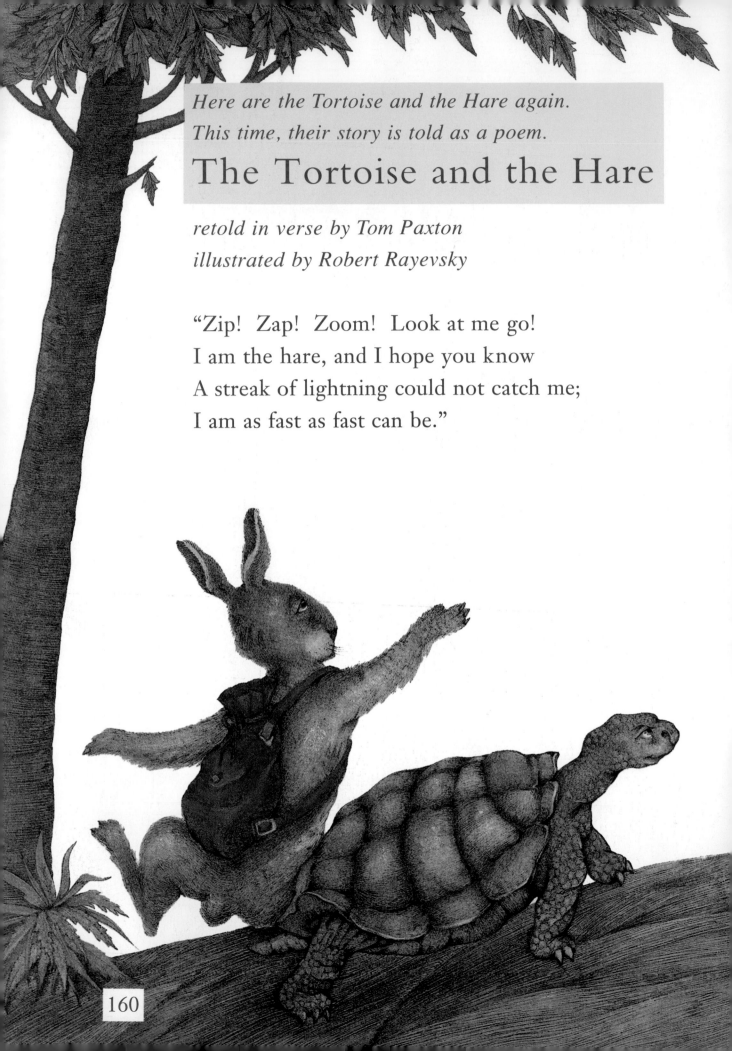

Here are the Tortoise and the Hare again.
This time, their story is told as a poem.

The Tortoise and the Hare

retold in verse by Tom Paxton
illustrated by Robert Rayevsky

"Zip! Zap! Zoom! Look at me go!
I am the hare, and I hope you know
A streak of lightning could not catch me;
I am as fast as fast can be."

"Fast, indeed," the tortoise replied,
"And yet, I wonder, if I tried
To win a race, how well I'd do.
I think I'd like to race with you."

"To race with me is lunacy!
Just search through all of history;
No greater mismatch you'll find there
Than a tortoise racing against a hare."

But the tortoise insisted on racing, and so
The starter cried, "Get ready! Go!"
Then Whiz! Bang! Boom! In a streak of light,
The hare was quickly out of sight.

163

Zip! Zoom! and Whiz! and Wham! and Screech!
"I guess this race is out of reach,"
The hare exclaimed as he stopped by a tree.
"That tortoise will never catch up with *me*."

He stretched out under the sunny skies,
And very soon had closed his eyes.
He slept and dreamt of carrot pie,
While the tortoise slowly plodded by.

The hare awoke and washed his face,
Then quickly finished up the race,
When — what a shock for Mister Hare! —
He found the tortoise waiting there!

To cheers that rang across the skies,
The tortoise took the winner's prize.
Yes, many there are who race and run,
But slow and steady gets things done.

The Lion and the Mouse

a play retold by Robert Hoffer

illustrated by S.D. Schindler

Characters: Lion

Mouse

Hunter 1

Hunter 2

Hunter 3

Hunter 4

Hunter 5

Scene 1

(The setting is a clearing in a forest. Lion enters the clearing and sits down.)

Lion: GRR-ROWF! Am I tired! *(He gives his mane a shake.)* It's not easy being the King of Beasts! Roaring all day, roaring all night. Making sure those little animals know who's boss . . . *(He yawns.)* I think it's time to take a little nap.

(Lion lies down and begins to snore.)

(Mouse enters from the left.)

Mouse: Chew and nibble, nibble and chew . . . mousing around is fun to do . . .

(Mouse *sees* Lion *and stops.*)

Mouse: Oh no! It's the Lion! I'd better get out of here! *(Pause)* Wait a second. He's asleep.

(Mouse *goes a little nearer.*)

Mouse: Wow. This is the closest I've ever come to the King of Beasts. I wonder if I can go even closer. *(He sings softly:)* Rock-a-bye Lion, in the treetop . . . Look at this! I'm standing on his tail! And now I'm standing on his paw! And now —

Lion: Aha! I've got you!

Mouse: Oh, no! I've been caught by the lion — my worst nightmare!

Lion: Oh boy! I've captured a mouse — my favorite snack!

Mouse: Wait! Stop! Please, don't eat me!

Lion: Why shouldn't I eat you? You woke me up, didn't you?

Mouse: Yes, I did, and I'm very sorry.

Lion: You stood on my paw, didn't you?

Mouse: I'll never do it again, I promise.

Lion: I know you won't do it again, because I'm going to eat you right now.

Mouse: No, wait. Don't do that. Listen — if you let me go, I'll . . . I'll . . .

Lion: Yes? What will you do?

Mouse: I'll be your friend for life.

Lion *(Chuckling):* My friend for life! Oh, what an honor!

Mouse: I'm serious! A mouse can be a very valuable friend to have! Maybe I can help you sometime.

Lion *(Laughing): You* help *me?* Oh, that's a good one. That's the best joke I've heard all week! A teensy little mouse helping the King of Beasts! *(Lion laughs some more.)* Mouse, do you know something? You've put me in such a good mood with your joke, I'm going to let you go.

Mouse: That is a wise decision! You won't be sorry! Remember, anytime you need me, just give a roar! *(Mouse scurries off.)*

Lion: Oh, I will, don't worry. *(To himself)* A mouse helping a lion. What a ridiculous idea! *(Lion curls up and goes back to sleep, still chuckling.)*

Scene 2

(The setting is another part of the forest, a few days later.)

Hunter 1: Shh . . . I think I hear him coming.

Hunter 2: Who?

Hunter 3: The lion!

Hunter 4: Are we catching a lion? Oops — I just remembered something I forgot to do at home.

172

Hunter 5: Come back here and be quiet . . .

(Lion *enters from the right.*)

Lion: All right, make way, make way. Here comes the King of Beasts. Give me some room.

(Hunters *come rushing out and throw a net over* Lion.)

Lion: Hey, what's going on? Get this thing off me!

Hunter 1: We've got him! We've got him!

Hunter 3: Quick, tie him down!

Hunter 4: You tie him down. I'll keep an eye out for tigers.

Hunter 5: Come on! Get busy and hammer down these ropes.

Hunter 2: Watch out for his claws!

Hunter 1: There! That does it. Now, let's go find a cage.

Hunter 4: I have a birdcage.

Hunter 5: Not a birdcage. A lion cage!

Hunter 2: Shouldn't one of us stay here and guard him?

Hunter 3: Don't be silly. He can't escape from those ropes.

(Hunters *exit*.)

Lion: Help! This is terrible! Me — the King of
Beasts — caught like a mouse in a trap! Oh, the
shame of it all! The humiliation! *(Lion roars.)*
(Mouse enters from the left.)

Mouse: Did you roar, Lion?

Lion: Oh, it's you, is it? All right, go ahead, Mouse.
Have your laugh. The mighty King doesn't look
so mighty now, does he? *(Lion starts to cry.)* Oh,
woe and misery! It's the zoo for mc! They'll lock
me up and throw away the key!
*(Mouse walks around Lion, rubbing his chin,
nodding to himself.)*

Mouse: Hmm, let me see. Yes, these shouldn't be any
     problem. I'll just start with this one . . .

Lion: *(He stops crying.)* What are you doing, Mouse?

Mouse: Chew and nibble, nibble and chew . . .
     gnawing on ropes is fun to do . . .

Lion: You're chewing through the ropes!

Mouse: That's one . . .

Lion: Mouse! Wonderful!

Mouse: That's two . . .

Lion: Hurry! They'll soon be back with a cage!

Mouse: And that's the last one.

Lion: I'm free! Mouse! You did it!

Mouse: Just in time, too. Here they come.

Lion: Quick, let's hide behind this bush!

(Hunters *enter from the left.*)

Hunter 1: Okay, Mr. Lion. Here's your new — Hey!

Hunter 2: He's gone!

Hunter 3: It looks as if he gnawed through the ropes.

Hunter 4: I didn't know lions gnawed.

Hunter 5: This is all your fault! I told you we should have guarded him!

Hunter 1 (*Pointing at* Hunter 2): It was those knots you made!

Hunter 2: My knots were fine!

Hunter 3: They were not!

Hunter 5: Yours were so loose a mouse could have escaped from them!

(Lion *steps out from behind bushes.*)

Hunter 4: Um . . . fellows. I think we have company.

Lion: ROARRR!

Hunters: Let's get out of here!

(Hunters *exit in a hurry.*)

Lion (*Yelling after them*): And don't come back!

Mouse: — or else!

Lion (*Turning to* Mouse): Mouse, you really came
through for me. (Lion *puts out his paw.*)
Thanks, pal.

Mouse (*Shaking* Lion's *paw*): Didn't I tell you that a
　　mouse can be a valuable friend to have?

Lion: You sure did. Today I learned that a small
　　friend can be a great friend. (Lion *snaps his*
　　fingers.) Hey, I just remembered! I have two
　　pieces of cheesecake in the refrigerator. Will you
　　join me, Mouse?

Mouse: I'd be delighted, Lion.

　　(*They put their arms around each other and exit to*
　　the right.)

A Tale of Two Friends

Did it seem strange to you that a lion and a mouse became friends? Think of another pair of animals that would make strange friends — a cat and a bird? a pig and a giraffe? Make up a story about how the two animals become friends. Tell how one helps the other.

Meet the Author

Robert Hoffer says that Aesop's fables are just right for turning into plays. "They usually have two animal characters, and at least one of them has a funny or interesting problem," he says. Hoffer has written several plays for children. Many of them are about animals with funny or interesting problems. They include *The Groundhog's Shadow*, *Rudolf the Red-Nosed Genius*, and *Rabbit, Rabbit*.

The Boy Who Cried **Wolf**

retold by Katherine Evans   *illustrated by Brad Teare*

There was once a young boy named Peter. He lived with his grandfather, a poor shepherd, who was growing very old.

All they owned in the world was a flock of sheep, which the old shepherd prized highly.

The time came when the grandfather could no longer take the sheep to the green meadow on the hill.

One day, he said to Peter, "My grandson, you have grown to be a fine, big boy. It is time for you to take the sheep to the meadow. My legs are old and stiff."

Peter did not want to leave his playmates in the village. But his grandfather had always been very kind to him. So he said, "I will gladly take the sheep to the meadow, Grandfather."

"Watch them carefully," said the grandfather. "They are all we own in the world."

Peter took the flock of fat, white sheep to the beautiful green meadow on the hill. Here, he sat under an olive tree, and guarded his flock while they grazed on the hillside.

He looked down into the village. He saw the villagers going about their daily tasks. He saw the farmer hoeing his cabbages. The farmer's sons were racing with their dog. Peter watched some boys fishing from the river bank. He heard the milkmaid singing as she carried her pails of milk to market.

Peter said to himself, "How lonely it is here, so high and far away from everyone."

Then one day, he had an idea. As soon as the sheep had started to graze on the hillside, Peter ran down the hill and called: "A wolf! A wolf!"

The villagers left their tasks and ran to the hill. The farmer stopped his work and ran. His sons and their dog ran after him. The boys who were fishing in the river ran as fast as they could, waving their fishing poles. The milkmaid with her pails of milk ran up the hill.

When they reached the top, they were all out of breath. But instead of finding a wolf, they found Peter lying under the olive tree. He laughed and laughed. "It's all a joke," he said.

They were all happy that there was no wolf. But they were very unhappy about running so hard and so fast for nothing.

Peter felt lonelier than before. A few days later he thought, "I'll try it again. What fun to have everyone come running." He put his hands to his mouth and called as loud as he could: "Help, help, a wolf! A wolf!"

Again the villagers left their tasks. Again the farmer stopped his work. He and his sons, and the boys fishing by the river, and the milkmaid all grabbed sticks and ran to help. This time, when they found the sheep grazing, and Peter rolling on the grass laughing, they were very angry.

One day, not long afterwards, Peter was sitting alone under the olive tree. Looking around him, he saw a big gray wolf. Sly and wicked it was, crouching behind the bushes at the top of the hill. The wolf's eyes gleamed as it watched the fat sheep, and its long red tongue hung out of its mouth.

Peter was so frightened that he could hear his heart beat louder and faster. He jumped up and shouted to the villagers: "A wolf! A wolf!"

But everyone in the village said: "That Peter! He's calling wolf again. This time, we will pay no attention to him." The farmer did not stop hoeing his cabbages. His sons went on playing with their dog. The boys sat on the river bank fishing. The milkmaid did not stop her singing.

Poor Peter called and called again. He tried to frighten the wolf away. But the wolf was not afraid of one small boy. The wolf sprang from the bushes and killed most of the boy's flock. The rest of the sheep ran away and were never seen again.

When people in the village heard that this time there really had been a wolf, they shook their heads and said: **"A liar will not be believed, even when he speaks the truth."**

Bring the Story to Life

Many storytellers have retold the story
"The Boy Who Cried Wolf." Now it's your
turn. With a group, act out the story. Take
the parts of Peter, his grandfather, the
villagers, and the wolf. Make up the words
they say.

Meet the Author

Katherine Evans wrote and illustrated many popular children's books. Her books include some exciting retellings of Aesop's fables and some folktales. Other books by Katherine Evans that you may enjoy are *A Bundle of Sticks*, *A Camel in the Tent*, and *The Man, the Boy, and the Donkey*.

Fable Favorites

Once in a Wood:
Ten Tales from Aesop
by Eve Rice
Read some of your favorite fables
again and some new ones too in this
beautiful book of fables.

Aesop's Fables
by Michael Hague
Here you will find some
familiar fable faces, such
as the fox and the crow.
You might meet some new
ones too.

The Hare and the Tortoise
by Caroline Castle
In this retelling, the hare is an
athlete and the tortoise is a writer.
The race is on!

The Goose That Laid the Golden Egg

by Geoffrey Patterson
A goose and a golden egg
turn the lives of two
happy farmers
upside-down in this fable.

The Wolf Who Cried Boy

by Jeffrey Dinardo
In this book,
wolves are afraid
of little boys.
When a nasty
little wolf cries
"Boy!" will his
friends come to
help him?

BOOK 4

IN and OUT of TROUBLE

There's nothing but trouble for the characters in this book. Tye May gets into trouble when she won't help a greedy emperor. Curious George gets caught in a room full of soapsuds. Mandy and Mimi get all wrapped up with the mummies at the museum. All of this certainly spells T – R – O – U – B – L – E. You'll read how the characters in this book get into trouble and how they get out of it.

CONTENTS

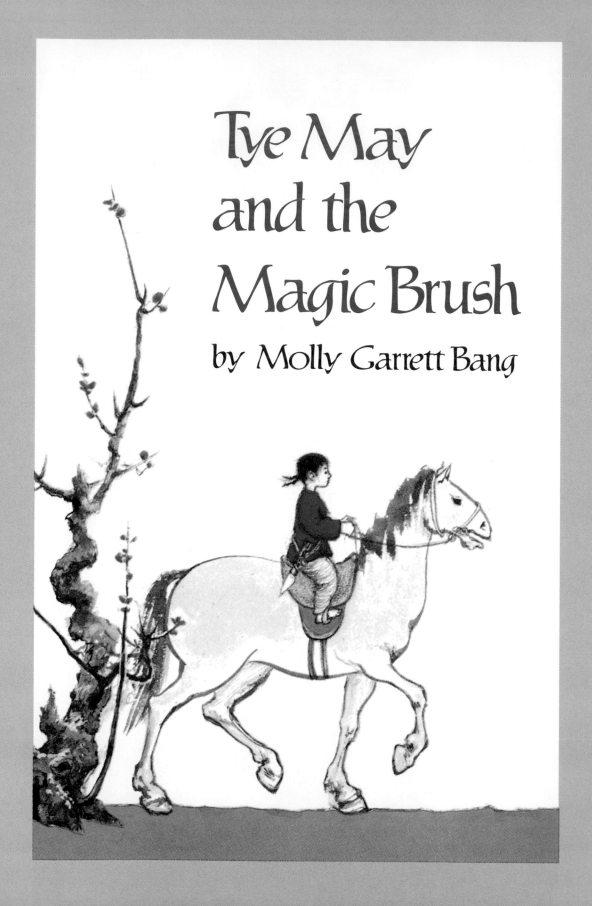

Tye May
and the
Magic Brush

by Molly Garrett Bang

1. Tye May Learns to Draw

Many years ago a cruel and greedy emperor ruled over China. His people were very poor. One of the poorest was Tye May. Her mother and father were dead and she lived alone. Every day she gathered firewood and cut reeds to sell in the marketplace.

One day Tye May passed by the school. She saw the teacher painting and stopped to watch. She knew, right then, that was what she wanted to do.

"Please, sir," she said to the teacher, "I would like to learn how to paint, but I have no money to buy a brush. Would you lend me one?"

The teacher turned red with anger. "Beggar girls don't paint," he said. "Get out of here!"

But Tye May had an iron will. She decided to make pictures her own way. Now when she gathered firewood, she used the sticks to draw animals in the dirt. When she cut reeds, she drew fish

on the rocks with her wet fingers. Soon she drew so well that her pictures looked almost alive.

When people saw her drawings of fish, they thought the fish would swim away. When they saw her pictures of birds, they thought the birds were going to sing.

But still Tye May had no brush. Every night she thought how happy she would be if she could have one.

2. The Magic Brush

Tye May worked especially hard one day, and drew until late at night. She fell into a deep sleep. A woman appeared and held out a brush to her. "This is a magic brush," the woman said. "Use it carefully."

Tye May took it in her hands. The brush was soft and thick, and the handle was of glittering gold. It felt heavy and good. "Thank you, thank you," she cried. But the woman was gone.

Tye May woke up. It was dawn. She looked around. Everything was the same. She saw the same dirt floor, the same broken walls, the same straw mat. It had all been a dream.

But what was this brush in her hands? Tye May was lost in wonder. She painted a bird. The bird flew up, perched outside her window, and began to sing to her. It was alive! She ran outside and painted a fish. The fish flipped its tail, jumped into the river, and splashed in the water for her to see. Tye May was happy.

3. The Wicked Landlord

Soon Tye May began to use the brush to make things for the poor. For a weaver she painted a loom. For a farmer she painted a hoe, a pail, and an oxcart.

Before long, a wicked landlord heard about the magic brush. He sent for Tye May. "Paint me a picture," he ordered. Tye May refused. The landlord shut her in an empty stable.

That night it began to snow. It snowed for three days. "Now she is cold and hungry," thought the wicked landlord. "Now she will paint for me." He unlocked the stable door.

Tye May was sitting in front of a warm stove, eating hot cakes! They smelled delicious, too. The landlord shook with rage. He ordered six strong men to kill the girl and bring him the magic brush. Tye May heard the men coming. She painted herself a horse and galloped away down the road.

The landlord and his men mounted their horses and galloped after her. They were coming closer and closer. Tye May stopped her horse. She jumped down and painted a big net on the road. The horses rode into it, and the men were tangled in the ropes. Tye May tied up the net and rode away.

4. The Evil Emperor

Tye May rode on for days and nights until she came to a distant town. She decided to paint pictures and sell them in the marketplace. But she knew it would not be safe to let people know about the magic brush. She painted birds without beaks and foxes with three legs. Because the pictures were not whole they could not come to life. No one found out what the magic brush could do.

One spring day, Tye May painted a crane, and left out its eyes, as usual. But as she passed the brush over the picture, two drops of ink fell onto the bird's head.

They became eyes. The crane opened them, lifted its wings, and flew off over the marketplace. Everyone stared after the bird. Now the secret was known.

The Emperor was told,
and he sent his officers to bring
Tye May to court. Tye May knew that this Emperor
was greedy and cruel to the poor. She hated him.

"Paint me a dragon," the Emperor commanded.
Tye May painted a toad. "Paint me a firebird," he
commanded. Tye May painted a rooster. The rooster
crowed and flew onto the Emperor's head. The toad
hopped onto his belly. They flew and hopped all over
the palace. The Emperor was furious. He grabbed the
magic brush and had Tye May thrown into prison.

5. The Emperor Tries the Brush

The greedy Emperor tried to use the brush himself. He painted a big gold brick. But it was too short. He painted another. It was still too short. Then he painted a long, long, long, long golden brick, as long as the whole scroll of paper.

At once the golden brick became a golden python. It opened its red mouth and slid toward the Emperor. The Emperor fainted, and the snake disappeared. The Emperor woke up and trembled. The Emperor set Tye May free and begged her to paint for him.

He promised her gold and silver. He promised her silks and jewels. He promised her a handsome prince. Tye May pretended to agree.

"What would you like me to paint?" she asked.

The Emperor thought about this. He was still very greedy. He wanted something big, but he was also afraid. If he asked for a mountain, wild beasts might come out of it and eat him up.

"Paint me the ocean," he commanded.

Tye May painted the ocean. It was wide and calm, and smooth as a jade mirror. The water was so clear the Emperor could see to the very bottom.

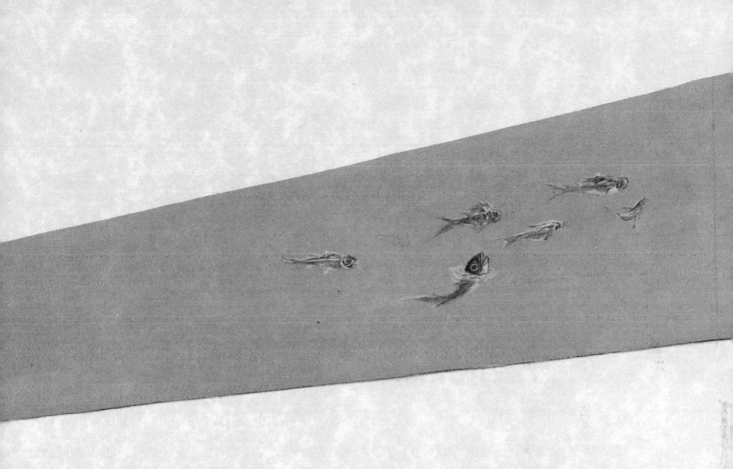

"Why are there no fish?" he asked.

Tye May made a few dots. The dots became fish of all the colors of the rainbow. They wiggled their tails, splashed back and forth, and swam slowly out to sea. The Emperor watched happily.

"Paint me a boat," he commanded. "I want to sail out and watch those fish."

Tye May painted a great ship. The Emperor and Empress, the Princes and Princesses, and all their court went on board. Tye May painted a few strokes. A breeze blew, ripples appeared on the water, and the ship moved off.

6. The Storm

The ship sailed too slowly for the Emperor. He stood on the bow and called to shore, "Make the wind blow stronger. Stronger!"

Tye May painted a few strokes. A strong wind began to blow and the seas grew rough. Tye May painted on. The wind howled, the waves rose higher, and the ship began to roll.

"Enough wind!" the Emperor shouted. "Enough! Enough!"

Tye May paid no attention. The winds blew into a terrible storm and drove the ship across the ocean to a lonely island. The ship crashed on the rocks, and the Emperor and his court almost drowned.

No ships came to the island and they were never rescued. They had to work hard every day, and were poor all the rest of their lives.

The story of Tye May and her magic brush was told throughout the land. But what became of her? No one knows for certain. Some say that she returned to the village where she was born. Others say she still walks from place to place, and paints for the poor wherever she goes.

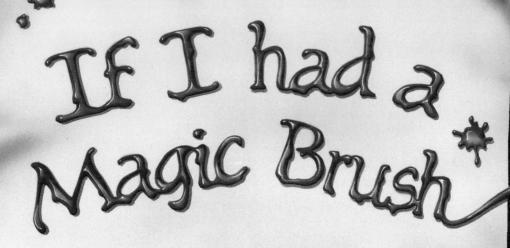

If I had a Magic Brush

Tye May had a magic brush that made her paintings come to life. If you had a magic brush, what would you like to paint that would come to life? Make a list of two or three things to paint. Then draw or paint the things on your list.

About the Author

Molly Garrett Bang

As a child, Molly Garrett Bang dreamed that someday she would illustrate books. When she was older, she moved to Japan to study Japanese painting. After she returned to the United States, her dream of becoming a book illustrator came true.

At first Molly Garrett Bang illustrated some folktales and stories her mother wrote. These books were so well liked that she started writing and illustrating her own books. You may enjoy reading her book, *The Paper Crane,* the story of a generous man whose bad luck changes when a magical paper animal comes to life.

Curious George
gets a medal
by
H. A. REY

This is George.

He lived with his friend, the man with the yellow hat. He was a good little monkey — but he was always curious.

George was alone this morning, looking at a picture book, when the doorbell rang.

It was the mailman.

"Here is a letter for you," he said. "Put it on your friend's desk. He'll read it to you when he comes home."

George was curious. It was not often that somebody wrote him. Too bad he could not read the letter — but maybe he could write one himself! In the top drawer of the desk there was paper and ink and a fountain pen.

George sat down on the floor
and began to write — but the pen
was dry. It needed ink; George
would have to fill it. He
got a funnel from the
kitchen and started
pouring ink . . .

But instead of going
into the pen the ink spilled all over and made
a big blue puddle on the floor. It was an awful mess.

Quickly George got the blotter from the desk, but
that was no help; the puddle grew bigger all the time.
George had to think of something else.

Why, soap and water — that's what you clean up
with! From the kitchen shelf he got a big box of soap
powder and poured all the powder over the ink. Then
he pulled the garden hose through the window, opened
the tap, and sprayed water on the powder.

Bubbles began to form, and then some lather, and more lather and more lather AND MORE LATHER. In no time the whole room was full of lather — so full, indeed, that George had to escape in a hurry . . .

When he was safely out of the house, he first turned off the tap. But what next? How could he get rid of all the lather before his friend came home?

George sat down in the grass and thought for a long time. Finally he had an idea: he would get the big shovel and shovel the lather out of the window!

But where WAS the lather? While George had been outside thinking, it had all turned into water. Now the room looked like a lake and the furniture like islands in it.

The shovel was no use. A pump was what George needed to get the water out, and he knew just where to find one: he had seen a portable pump at the farm down the road.

The farmer was away working in the fields. Nobody noticed George when he got the pump out of the shed.

It was heavy. He would need help to pull it all the way back to the house.

Maybe he could tie the goat to the pump and make her pull it? But just as George was about to slip the loop over the goat's head — he was hurled through the air and landed near a pen full of pigs.

The biggest pig was standing near the gate. What if George opened the gate just enough to let him out? A big pig could easily pull a small pump.

Carefully, George lifted the latch — and before he knew it, ALL the pigs had burst out of the pen, grunting and squealing and trying to get away as fast as they could. George was delighted. He had never seen anything like it. For the moment all his troubles were forgotten . . .

But now the pigs were all gone, and not a single one was left to help him with the pump.

Luckily, there were cows grazing nearby. Cows were gentle and strong. It would mean nothing to a cow to pull the pump for him.

This time George was right; the cow did not mind being tied to the pump. She even let him climb on her back — and off they went! George was glad. Now he would soon be home, pump out the room, and everything would be all right.

Meanwhile the farmer and his son had heard the squealing of the pigs. They rushed home from the fields and now had their hands full catching all the pigs. Not until the last pig was safely back in the pen did they have time to look around. And what did they see? A little monkey riding on their cow, making off with their pump!

The chase was on! George and the cow were ahead at first. But the pump was slowing them down. The farmers were getting closer and closer. Now they had almost caught up with them — but WHERE WAS GEORGE?

Here he was — hiding in a shirt! The farmers had run past him. But on their way home they had to come back over the same road. George did not feel safe in his hiding place . . . Just then a truck came rattling down the road.

George jumped aboard (monkeys are good at jumping) and was gone before the farmers had a chance to see him.

The truck drove to a part of town that George had never seen before. At last it stopped in front of a large building. It was the Museum. George did not know what a museum was. He was curious. While the guard was busy reading his paper, George slipped inside.

He walked up the steps and into a room full of all sorts of animals. At first George was scared, but then he noticed that they did not move. They were not alive. They were stuffed animals, put into the Museum so that everybody could get a good look at them.

DINOSAUR (EXTINCT)

In the next room George saw something so enormous it took his breath away. It was a dinosaur. George was not scared this time; he knew it was not real. He looked at the dinosaur and then at the baby dinosaur — and then he saw the palm tree full of nuts. George liked nuts. Suddenly he felt very hungry (he had missed lunch that day). He would climb up and . . .

Do not touch!

BABY DINOSAUR

Just then he heard footsteps. He had to hide again — but where?

A family came in to take a look at the dinosaur. They paid no attention to the little monkey who was standing there. The monkey did not move. He stood so still they thought he was just another stuffed animal . . .

George was glad when they were gone! Now he could pick the nuts. He climbed up the dinosaur's neck and started to pull, but the nuts would not come off (George did not know they were not real either). He pulled harder and harder, the tree began to sway . . .

CRASH! Down came the tree on the dinosaur's head, down came the dinosaur, and down came George!

Guards came rushing in from all sides, and underneath the fallen dinosaur they found a little monkey! They pulled him out of there and brought him to Professor Wiseman, who was the director of the Museum. Professor Wiseman was terribly angry. "Lock that naughty monkey up right away," he said, "and take him back to the zoo. He must have run away from there."

George was carried off in a cage. He felt so ashamed he almost wished he were dead . . . Suddenly the door opened. "George!" somebody shouted. It was his friend, the man with the yellow hat! "It seems you got yourself into a lot of trouble today," he said. "But maybe this letter here will get you out of it. It's from Professor Wiseman; he needs your help for an experiment. I found it on my desk at home; but I couldn't find YOU anywhere, so I came over here to talk to the Professor."

And this is what the letter said:

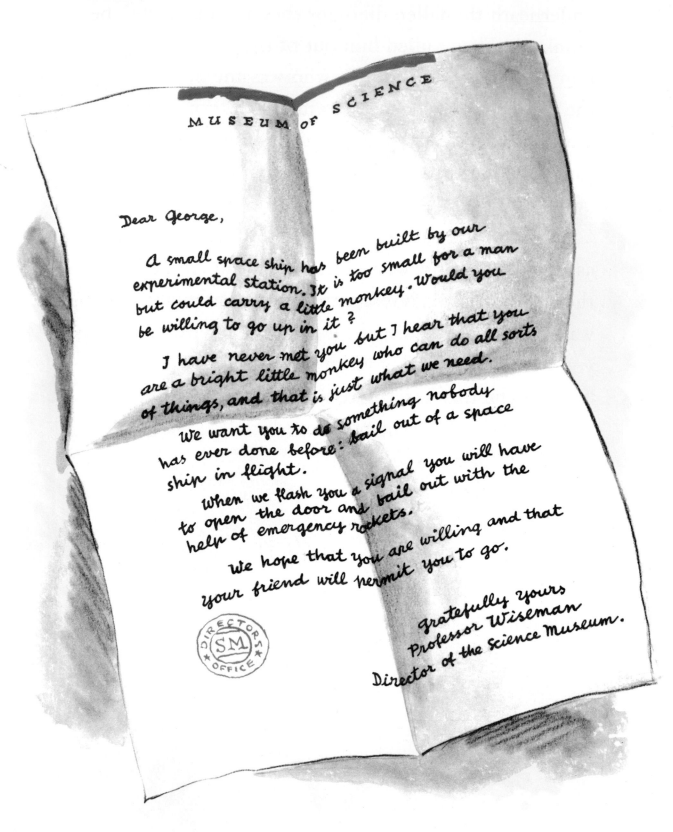

MUSEUM OF SCIENCE

Dear George,

A small space ship has been built by our experimental station. It is too small for a man but could carry a little monkey. Would you be willing to go up in it?

I have never met you but I hear that you are a bright little monkey who can do all sorts of things, and that is just what we need.

We want you to do something nobody has ever done before: bail out of a space ship in flight.

When we flash you a signal you will have to open the door and bail out with the help of emergency rockets.

We hope that you are willing and that your friend will permit you to go.

Gratefully yours
Professor Wiseman
Director of the Science Museum.

"So YOU are George!" Professor Wiseman said.
"If I had only known . . . Of course everything will be
forgiven, if you are willing to go."

They got the smallest size space suit for George
and all the other things he needed for the flight. Then
they helped him put them on and showed him how to
use them. When everything was ready, a truck drove
up with a special television screen mounted on it to
watch the flight. They all got on and were off to the
launching site. They checked all the controls of the
space ship, especially the lever that opened the door.
George tried it, too.

The great moment had come. George waved good-by and went aboard. The door was closed. Professor Wiseman began to count: "Five — four — three — two — one — GO!"

He pressed the button and the ship rose into the air, slowly first, and then faster and faster and higher and higher, until they could no longer see it in the sky. But on the screen they saw George clearly all the time.

Now the moment had come for George to bail out. Professor Wiseman flashed the signal. They watched the screen: George did not move. Why didn't he pull the lever? In a few seconds it would be too late. The ship would be lost in outer space, with George in it!

They waited anxiously . . . At last George began to move.

Slowly, as if in a daze, he was groping for the lever. Would he reach it in time? There — he had grabbed it! The door opened — hurrah — George was on his way!

228

Out of the blue an open parachute came floating down to earth. The truck raced over to the spot where George would land.

What a welcome for George!

Professor Wiseman hung a big golden medal around his neck. "Because," he said, "you are the first living being to come back to earth from a space flight." And on the medal it said: To George, the First Space Monkey.

Then a newspaperman took his picture and everybody shouted and cheered, even the farmer and his son, and the kind woman from next door (who had worked for hours to get the water out of the room).

"I'm proud of you, George," said the man with the yellow hat. "I guess the whole world is proud of you today."

It was the happiest day in George's life.

SPEECH, SPEECH!

The crowd roared when Professor
Wiseman gave Curious George his medal.
Think about the things Curious George did
to earn the medal. Next, decide what Professor
Wiseman might have said to him when he
gave George the medal. Write down
a few ideas first. Then say your
speech to a group of your
classmates.

ABOUT THE AUTHOR

H. A. Rey

H. A. Rey spent most of his free time as a child drawing the animals at a nearby zoo. When he grew up, he wrote many books about a friendly monkey called Curious George.

You can follow more of George's adventures in the following books:

Curious George Takes a Job Imagine Curious George as a window washer or a painter. As usual, his curiosity gets him into trouble.

Curious George Rides a Bike The man with the yellow hat has given George a new bike. George promised he would stay close to home, but . . .

Cecily G. and the Nine Monkeys Cecily G. is a lonely giraffe until Curious George and his family come to stay with her.

THE MUDDLE

In the middle of the muddle is me.
It's a place where I am very apt to be.
I get myself all straightened out
    And then
I'm right back in the muddle
    Again.

Marchette Chute

LOST AT THE ZOO

If I were lost
Inside the zoo,
I think that this
Is what I'd do.

I'd say, "Giraffe,
Please look around —
Your head is high
Above the ground.

"Will you point out
To me the place
Where you can see
My mother's face?"

I'm sure Giraffe
Would find my mama,
Looking at an elk
Or llama.

I'd leap to her
Like a kangaroo,
And never get lost
Again at the zoo!

Ilo Orleans

M & M
and
The Mummy Mess

By Pat Ross ▪ Illustrations by Marylin Hafner

It was Saturday morning. Mandy and Mimi, the friends M and M, were going to the natural history museum together.

They knew this museum very well. When they were babies, their mothers brought them there in strollers.

"Remember how we used to think the giant whales would get us?" said Mandy.

"Babies aren't so smart," sighed Mimi.

The friends M and M still went to the museum, but now they went without their mothers.

They still visited the whales. They never missed the dinosaurs. And they always quacked at the stuffed birds. But not this time. This time they were going for the new show that opened at noon. M and M wanted to be the first in line for Mummy Wonders.

They'd read a lot about mummies. But they had never seen one.

When they passed a water fountain, Mandy and Mimi stopped for a drink.

"Promise you won't laugh if I tell you a secret?" said Mandy.

"I promise," said Mimi, who liked secrets.

"Well," Mandy whispered, "sometimes I think mummies are too creepy. And maybe they're just pretending to be dead."

Mimi started to laugh. Then she remembered her promise.

"These mummies have been dead for thousands of years," Mimi told Mandy.

"What about that mummy movie we saw on TV?" said Mandy. "First the mummies broke open their cases. Then they turned people like us into mummies."

"I *loved* that movie!" cried Mimi. "*Escape of the Doomed Mummies*. It was so disgusting. But it was only a movie."

"I sure hope so," said Mandy. "I like mummies, but not enough to be one."

The museum was filled with people. Mandy and Mimi looked for a sign about the new mummy show.

But the only sign in the lobby said:

"We've seen that," said Mandy.

"Five times," groaned Mimi.

Mandy checked the news clipping. It told all about the mummy show.

"It's in the East Hall," she told Mimi. So they headed for the East Hall.

On the way, the friends passed the stuffed birds without quacking.

They ran right past the dinosaur room without looking.

"Slow down," said Mandy. "There's nobody ahead of us." And it was true that the hallway leading to Mummy Wonders was empty.

The closer they got to the East Hall, the darker it got.

When they rounded the corner, they knew something was wrong.

The East Hall was very quiet. There was a rope across the doorway, and a sign that said:

Mandy and Mimi had been waiting all week. How could Mummy Wonders be closed?

Mandy read the news story again.

"Oh, no," she said, showing the story to Mimi. "I was so excited, I got the date wrong."

"The big day is *next* Saturday," said Mimi sadly, reading over Mandy's shoulder.

Mandy stuffed the clipping in her pocket and started to go.

"Wait!" cried Mimi. "I'll bet they wouldn't mind if we had a sneak preview. You know, that's when certain people get in ahead of everybody else."

Mandy and Mimi looked beyond the ropes. They could see wooden cases.

And they were sure they could see real mummies at the back of the room.

"Museums like kids to be curious," said Mandy.

So the friends ducked under the rope and went into the hall of Mummy Wonders alone.

"It's dark," said Mandy.

"That's just to get you in the mood," said Mimi.

"It sure is working," said Mandy.

"Hey," Mimi went on cheerfully, "what did the child say to its mummy?"

"Okay, what?" asked Mandy, feeling better now.

"Unwrap me. I'm dying in here!" cried Mimi, who loved mummy jokes.

M and M's laughter echoed in the big, dark room.

The two friends made their way to the back of the room. They were sure the real mummies were there.

They passed one long, wooden mummy case after another.

Then, all of a sudden, M and M saw three strange bodies standing against the wall. And they were not mummies.

"They're *dummies*," said Mandy. "Like the ones you see undressed in store windows. I wonder what they're doing here." Then they saw a sign that said:

Next to the sign was a big roll of cloth, very much like the cloth that real mummies are wrapped in.

"I've got it," said Mimi. "They're going to wrap the dummies to make mummies. Let's check this out."

So Mandy and Mimi stopped and looked at the wrapping cloth.

"It looks like bandages," said Mimi. "Let's see how it works. Stand still."

So Mandy stood still, with her arms out to the sides. And Mimi started to wrap.

Mimi wrapped Mandy's arms. She finished the first one quickly. "Hey, this is fun!" said Mandy.

"This is hard work," said Mimi.

She wrapped the second arm, then all five fingers on each hand.

"I wonder why they wrapped them," said Mimi, still working hard.

"I've got a book that tells all about it," said Mandy. "It was to keep their bodies from rotting and falling apart."

"Yuck," said Mimi, going on to Mandy's body.

Mandy could feel the cloth getting tighter and tighter.

"It's like a giant cast," said Mandy, who was wondering if being wrapped was really so much fun.

Mimi finished the body and went on to the legs.

"Why would anyone care so much about a yucky dead body?" Mimi wondered out loud.

"Well," said Mandy, glad she knew more than Mimi, "the ancient Egyptians were sure they went someplace else after they died."

"I get it!" cried Mimi, wrapping faster and tighter now. "And they wanted to make sure their bodies were ready for the trip."

"They even took their special things along," said Mandy, who felt an itch start on her elbow.

"I'd take my bottle cap collection," said Mimi.

"You couldn't even be a mummy," said Mandy.

"How come?" Mimi was finishing the legs now.

"Because only kings and queens and very important people could be mummies," Mandy explained.

"Well, maybe I would have been a princess. Then I'd get to take my bottle cap collection. You don't know," added Mimi.

"I do know — " began Mandy.

"*I* know," broke in Mimi, "that you sound like a mummy book somebody ought to shut!"

She laughed at her own joke.

"And besides," Mimi added, stepping back, "you're finished. I did a great job. You'll last a thousand years, at least."

"Maybe you did too good a job," said Mandy. "I can't bend my legs."

"Something's not quite right," said Mimi.

"I'm glad you noticed," said Mandy, feeling the itch start up again.

"I forgot the head."

"Not my face!" cried Mandy.

Soon, Mandy was wrapped from head to toe.

Just then, Mandy and Mimi heard voices in the hall. And the voices were headed their way.

"Oh, no! It's the people who work on the mummies," cried Mandy.

The voices got closer and closer.

"Don't move," whispered Mimi.

"I can't," whispered Mandy, trying to move her stiff
mummy legs.

Then Mimi hid behind a dummy. And Mandy
stood like a mummy.

The workers walked right past mummy Mandy,
who wondered if museum people really wanted
children to be *that* curious.

The workers walked past Mimi, who was hiding
behind a dummy. And Mimi wondered if sneak
previews were a good idea after all.

Then, all of a sudden, somebody patted mummy Mandy on the back. It was a tall man in a white coat. His name tag said DIRECTOR.

This is it! thought Mandy.

We've had it! thought Mimi.

"Who wrapped the short one?" asked the director. No one answered.

Then, from behind a dummy, came a funny little voice. "I did," it said.

"Nice work," said the director, looking at mummy Mandy. "It looks so real."

And then he walked away.

Quietly, Mimi tiptoed over.

"Shhh," she whispered. And she unwrapped Mandy's legs.

Then, as fast as they could, Mandy and Mimi ducked under the rope.

Mimi headed for the doorway. Mandy followed. The loose cloth flapped around her legs as she ran.

"Hey, you two!" someone shouted.

"We should stop," puffed Mandy.

"Let's find a ladies' room first," said Mimi. "Then we can talk about who read the date wrong and got us into this mummy mess." She looked hard at Mandy.

"We did it *together*!" said Mandy. "A mummy mess for both of us!"

"Okay," agreed Mimi, pointing to a narrow door with no sign. "In here! Quick!"

It was dark inside. And it smelled funny. It smelled like the science corner at school when the experiment went wrong.

"They don't keep the bathrooms very nice here," said Mimi.

She searched for the light switch. The room was dark. But over by a window, M and M could see a strange shape. It was hanging from the ceiling, upside-down. The shape did not look like anything that belonged in a bathroom. It looked like a huge bird that belonged in a zoo — behind bars.

Mimi found a row of switches. She turned them all on at once. Now the room was filled with light.

Mandy and Mimi could see the huge bird by the window, and hundreds of its strange friends — on shelves, in cases, and hanging, too.

"They're stuffed!" cried Mandy in relief.

"Like the birds we always quack at," cried Mimi. "This must be the room where they work on the birds for the museum. Wait till we tell our science class about this!"

"Wait till we tell our science class we got put in jail," said Mandy.

Suddenly Mimi looked worried. "We have to give ourselves up," she said. "And now."

Then Mimi took Mandy's hand. And without a word, the friends turned off the lights and left the bird room together.

They were headed back down the hall when they heard someone shout, "Stop that mummy!"

"Hey! You two!" cried a voice they knew from before.

And there was the man in the white coat with a
name tag that said DIRECTOR.

What the man saw was a mummy and a mummy's
friend, looking very upset. There was just no way to
hide the mummy mess they were in.

The director took one look and he started to say
something.

"We didn't mean — " broke in Mandy.

"My goodness," the director cried out. "A mummy
who talks!"

And he began to smile a little.

"We were just curious," said Mimi.

"Well, you do nice work," said the director, looking at Mimi's wrapping job. "But you're a week early!"

Then he looked serious and tapped his foot on the floor.

Suddenly it was very quiet.

Mandy and Mimi were afraid to say another word.

Then, "Didn't you see the signs?" the director asked more firmly.

Mandy and Mimi nodded their heads "Yes."

"And didn't you see the rope?" M and M were really worried now.

They hoped he hadn't seen them leave the rare bird room, too.

"And the bird room is no hiding place," he said.

M and M had been in messes before, but this was the worst.

"I think I know just the thing to keep two curious girls out of trouble," he said, more kindly.

Mimi began to unwrap Mandy.

"Don't unwrap your friend," said the director. "I have a plan."

Mandy was sure the director would leave her wrapped forever.

Mimi was sure the director would never let her come back.

"Follow me," said the director.

They passed the whales and the dinosaurs and the stuffed birds.

At last they came to the lobby.

There the director handed Mimi a stack of fliers to hand out. The fliers said:

COMING SOON

MUMMY WONDERS

THE MUSEUM OF NATURAL HISTORY

"We're really sorry," M and M said. And they meant it.

"I know," said the director. "But you gave me a great idea."

Then he made a sign and hung it on Mandy.

The sign said:

"You two should be the best kind of advertising for Mummy Wonders," he said.

So Mandy and Mimi gave out fliers. And they talked about wrapping mummies to the children.

M and M did such a good job that the director invited them back.

The very next Saturday, Mandy and Mimi came at noon.

They looked in on the whales. They waved at the dinosaurs. They quacked at stuffed birds.

And they took their places at the front of the line to see Mummy Wonders — without any mummy mess, this time.

Come One, Come All!

At the end of the story, Mimi and Mandy hand out fliers about the mummies at the museum. They also tell people about the show. What else could Mimi and Mandy say or do to get people to come to the mummy show? Think of some funny and clever ideas. Then act them out for your classmates.

About the Author

Pat Ross

Pat Ross began writing about Mandy and Mimi, two girls who are always in trouble, many years ago. She has said that many of her ideas for the Mandy and Mimi characters came from raising her daughter, Erica.

You can meet Mandy and Mimi again in the following books:

M & M and the Super Child Afternoon Mandy and Mimi want to take an after-school class together, but can't decide between their two favorites.

M & M and the Bad News Babies The girls are trying to earn money to buy a fish tank. Taking care of twins turns out to be an afternoon of trouble.

IN AND OUT OF BOOKS

Mouse Soup by Arnold Lobel

A little mouse must think quickly if he doesn't want to end up as dinner for a weasel.

Madeline's Rescue by Ludwig Bemelmans

Read how Madeline and her school friends get into one crazy adventure after another in Paris, France.

Me and Neesie by Eloise Greenfield

Janell's make-believe friend, naughty Neesie, is always getting into trouble. Will Janell give her up?

Katie Morag Delivers the Mail by Mairi Hedderwick

How can Katie get into trouble by delivering mail?
It all begins when she drops the mailbag into water.

Harry in Trouble by Barbara Ann Porte

Boy is Harry in trouble! He's lost his library card
three times in a row. But he soon finds out he is not
the only one who gets into jams.

Harry the Dirty Dog by Gene Zion

Harry is a white dog with black spots. After running
away, he comes back a black dog with white spots.
Will his family ever recognize him again?

Glossary

This glossary can help you find out the meanings of some of the words in this book. The meanings given are the meanings of the words as the words are used in the book. Sometimes a second meaning is also given.

A

advertise To call attention to: *We saw posters advertising a dinosaur show at the museum.*

allow To let happen or permit: *Josh is allowed to stay up late on Fridays.*

ancient Having to do with things that happened thousands of years ago: *Bob and Lisa went to see a movie about ancient mummies.*

artist A person who draws or paints pictures: *Mary is the artist who painted my picture.*

awful Very bad or unpleasant: *When his best friend went away for the summer, Joe felt awful.*

B

bail out To jump out of an aircraft with a parachute: *Judy bailed out of the airplane before it landed in a field.*

bandage A strip of cloth used to cover a cut: *Sam put a bandage over the cut on his knee.*

blink To close and open the eyes quickly: *I blinked my eyes when I went outside into the bright sun.*

brush A tool made of stiff hairs attached to a hard back or handle: *Beth used her new* **brush** *to paint a picture.*

brush

bumpy Covered with rough, rounded shapes: *The skin on a frog is smooth, it is not* **bumpy**.

cast A stiff bandage, usually made of cloth coated with plaster: *Fred is wearing a* **cast** *on his broken arm.*

cast

chalk A soft material used for making marks on a blackboard: *Susan used green* **chalk** *to draw a tree on the board.*

chew To grind or crush with the teeth: *Since mice have sharp teeth, they can* **chew** *through ropes.*

clutch To hold or grasp tightly: *Jane* **clutched** *the bat with both hands.*

come through To do what is needed: *The mouse* **came through** *for the lion by helping him escape from the hunters.*

contest A race, game, or other test in which the winner gets a prize: *A* **contest** *was held to see which frog could jump the greatest distance.*

copy To make something that is like or that looks like something else: *Most painters do not want to* **copy** *someone else's paintings. They want to paint something new.*

course The place where a race is held: *Last Saturday, there was a race on the new course behind the school.*

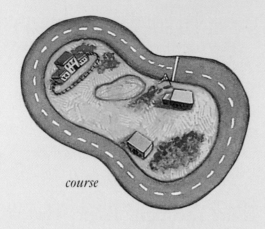

course

creepy Scary. Something that is creepy gives you a tingling feeling: *She thinks spiders are creepy.*

croak A low, rough sound, such as that made by a frog or a crow: *On summer nights, you can hear the croak of frogs in the pond.*

cruel Mean or unkind: *The cruel king made his helpers work day and night.*

cure To make a sick person well, or fix something that is wrong: *The medicine will cure your sore throat.*

curious Eager to find out about something: *Jeff took the clock apart because he was curious to see how it worked.*

D

disease An illness or sickness. Chicken pox is a disease that many children get.

dough A soft, thick mixture of water, flour, and other ingredients. Dough is used to make bread and other baked foods.

E

earn To receive payment for doing a job: *Max earned money for a new bicycle by washing windows.*

emperor A man who rules a country or many countries. An emperor is something like a king.

escape To get free or break loose: *My hamster escaped from its cage.*

260

favorite Someone or something that is liked more than anything else: *David has many shirts, but the blue one is his favorite.*

flight A trip in an airplane or space ship: *The flight would take the space ship into outer space.*

flock A group of one kind of animal. A flock lives, travels, and feeds together: *Every day the flock of sheep go up on the hill to feed.*

flock

fool with To play around with or take lightly: *Matches should not be fooled with.*

get rid of To free oneself from something that is not wanted: *We decided to get rid of the toys we don't use anymore.*

gnaw To chew or bite: *The dog gnawed on the bone.*

graze To feed on growing grass: *The cows grazed on the grassy hill.*

greedy Wanting more than one needs or deserves: *Jimmy wouldn't share the apples because he was greedy.*

guard To keep from danger: *The boy's job was to guard the sheep.*

guitar A stringed musical instrument that has a long neck and a body shaped like a pear.

guitar

261

hare An animal that looks very much like a rabbit. A hare is larger than a rabbit and has longer ears and legs.

honor A special right: *It was a great honor for Polly to meet the president.*

hum To make a low, soft sound like a long *m*, usually in the tune of a song: *Nora hummed her favorite song as she washed the dishes.*

humiliation A feeling of hurt pride or shame: *The humiliation of losing 47 to 3 made the players on the team want to quit.*

jealous Feeling angry or envious about something another person has or is doing: *Carl was jealous because I went camping and he couldn't go.*

jeans Pants made from a heavy cloth: *Larry put on his oldest jeans to clean out the attic.*

launching site The place from which a space ship is sent into space: *We went to the launching site to watch the space ship blast off.*

lesson Something to be learned: *Paul wanted to be a singer when he grew up, so he took singing lessons.*

liar A person who says things that are not true.

magic The art of using spells, charms, and special powers to make changes in nature or people: *Ned was sure the woman used magic to turn the scarf into a flower.*

meadow An area of grassy ground. Sheep or other animals often graze in a meadow.

medal A piece of metal given to someone who has done something special: *The firefighter received a medal for saving many lives.*

medal

misery Great pain or suffering: *Gail knew that her misery would not stop until she found a way to make her brother stop teasing her.*

mitt A large, padded glove that baseball players wear: *Emily hoped her new mitt would help her catch the baseball.*

mitt

monitor A student who does a special job to help the teacher: *The paper monitor passed out drawing paper to the whole class.*

museum A building for keeping and displaying interesting and valuable things: *The guide at the museum showed us a model of a huge dinosaur.*

N

neck The long, narrow connecting part of a guitar.

neck

nibble To eat with small, quick bites: *Little by little, a mouse can nibble through a rope.*

O

out Having lost your turn while playing a game: *Tom was called out because the pitcher caught the ball before it hit the ground.*

parachute A large piece of cloth used to slow the fall of a person who has jumped from an airplane or other high place.

parachute

part A role or a character in a play or movie: *Maria wants to play the **part** of the queen in the school play.*

pay attention To think about something or to listen carefully to someone: *The teacher asked the class to **pay attention** to what she was reading.*

peep To look quickly or secretly, especially from a hidden place. Peep means the same as peek.

perseverance Continuing to try to do something even though it is very difficult: *Jay was so tired that he wanted to give up, but his **perseverance** helped him win the race.*

piled up Stacked or put on top of each other: *A lot of books were **piled up** on the table.*

piled up

play reading Speaking out loud the lines from a play. To try out for a role in a play, you would take part in a play reading.

potion A drink used for medicine or magic: *The woman made a **potion** she said would make people smarter.*

powerful Very strong: *A lion is a **powerful** animal.*

price tag A small card that gives the price of an item in a store: *The price tag on the shirt read $20.00.*

price tag

property Something owned by someone: *These books are the property of the school.*

R

rage Very great anger: *The monkey shook with rage when the fox stole his bananas.*

recognize To know from past experience: *Sandy recognized her cousin even though she had not seen him for two years.*

remember To think of something again: *Pete remembered that he had to return his library books today.*

rescue To save from danger or harm: *The firefighter rescued my cat when it was caught in the tree.*

reserve To arrange ahead of time to buy or use something: *Carol wanted to be sure that she got one of the new puppies, so she reserved one before they were born.*

reward Something given in recognition of an achievement or hard work: *Anna was given a reward for finding the lost book.*

rot To spoil: *If you leave meat out on a hot day, it will rot.*

rule A statement that tells how something may or may not be done: *The rules for this game are written on the box.*

265

shepherd A person who takes care of a flock of sheep: *The **shepherd** made sure the sheep stayed together.*

sly Clever or tricky: *A fox is a **sly** animal.*

sneak preview An early showing of a movie, play, or show to a small group of people: *The school play will be performed Friday, but the students had a **sneak preview** for their parents on Wednesday.*

sneeze To force air through the mouth and nose suddenly: *When dust tickles your nose, it may cause you to **sneeze**.*

space ship A vehicle used for travel outside the earth's atmosphere. A space ship sometimes travels to the moon.

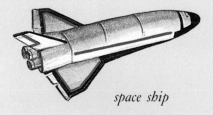

space ship

spirit Liveliness or pep: *Even though the team had lost two games in a row, they still had a lot of team **spirit**.*

strum To pluck the strings of a musical instrument: *Sue **strummed** a song on her guitar.*

strung To have put strings on a musical instrument: *Frank **strung** rubber bands across a box to make a toy guitar.*

supposed to To do what is expected or planned: *Ellen is **supposed to** practice her singing every day.*

swung Moved the arms to hit something: *Ralph **swung** his bat at the ball.*

tortoise A turtle that lives on land. A tortoise is a slow-moving animal that has four legs and a hard shell.

tortoise

tower A tall building or a tall part of a larger building: *The tower rose up above the other buildings.*

tower

traitor A person who is false to a friend, country, or idea.

trouble A difficult or upsetting problem: *Molly's trouble is that she worries too much.*

V

valuable Very important or useful: *A good friend is valuable.*

victory The winning of a contest or other competition: *After Elaine won the race, she celebrated her victory.*

W

wicked Evil or mean: *The wicked king threw his helpers in jail.*

wise Very smart: *The wise woman seemed to have the answer to every question.*

wonder A feeling of amazement: *Jack looked with wonder as the magician performed her tricks.*

worst Extremely bad: *All of the singers are bad, but he is the worst of all.*

wrap To cover with paper: *Rosa wrapped my presents with red paper.*

wrong Not right or true: *Nancy should have gone to first base, but she ran the wrong way.*

Acknowledgments

For each of the selections listed below, grateful acknowledgement is made for permission to excerpt and/or reprint original or copyrighted material, as follows:

Major Selections

The Art Lesson, written and illustrated by Tomie dePaola. Copyright © 1989 by Tomie dePaola. Reprinted by permission of G.P. Putnam's Sons. Crayola is a registered trademark of Binney & Smith Inc. Used with permission.

Best Friends, by Steven Kellogg. Copyright © 1986 by Steven Kellogg. Reprinted by permission of the publisher, Dial Books for Young Readers.

The Boy Who Cried Wolf, retold by Katherine Evans. Copyright © 1960, 1989 by Albert Whitman and Company. Reprinted by permission of Albert Whitman and Company.

Curious George Gets a Medal, by H.A. Rey. Copyright © 1957 by H.A. Rey. Copyright © renewed 1985 by Margaret E. Rey. Reprinted by permission of Houghton Mifflin Company.

Jasper Makes Music, by Betty Horvath. Copyright © 1967 by Franklin Watts. Reprinted by permission of Franklin Watts.

Josefina Finds the Prince, by Eve Bunting. Text copyright © 1976 by Eve Bunting. Reprinted by permission of the author.

The Lion and the Mouse, by Robert Hoffer. Reprinted by permission of the author.

M&M and The Mummy Mess, by Pat Ross. Text copyright © 1985 by Pat Ross. Illustrations copyright © 1985 by Marylin Hafner. Reprinted by permission of Viking Penguin, a division of Penguin Books USA, Inc., and Collins Publishers.

Now One Foot, Now the Other, written and illustrated by Tomie dePaola. Copyright © 1981 by Tomie dePaola. Reprinted by permission of G.P. Putnam's Sons.

Ronald Morgan Goes to Bat, by Patricia Reilly Giff. Text copyright © 1988 by Patricia Reilly Giff. Illustrations copyright © 1988 by Susanna Natti. Reprinted by permission of Viking Penguin, a division of Penguin Books USA, Inc.

Strega Nona's Magic Lessons, written and illustrated by Tomie dePaola. Copyright © 1982 by Tomie dePaola. Reprinted by permission of Harcourt Brace Jovanovich, Inc.

The Tortoise and the Hare, by Janet Stevens. Copyright © 1984 by Janet Stevens. All rights reserved. Reprinted by permission of Holiday House.

Tye May and the Magic Brush, by Molly Garrett Bang. Copyright © 1981 by Molly Garrett Bang. Reprinted by permission of Greenwillow Books, a division of William Morrow and Company, Inc.

Poetry

"Lost at the Zoo," by Ilo Orleans. Copyright © 1958 by Ilo Orleans. Reprinted by permission of Karen S. Solomon.

"The Muddle," by Marchette Chute, from *Rhymes About Us*. Copyright © 1974 by E.P. Dutton, Inc. Reprinted by permission of Mary Chute Smith.

"poem for rodney," by Nikki Giovanni, from *Spin a Soft Black Song*. Copyright © 1971, 1985 by Nikki Giovanni. Reprinted by permission of Farrar, Straus and Giroux.

"The Secret Place," written and illustrated by Tomie dePaola, from *Once Upon a Time*. Copyright © 1968 by G.P. Putnam's Sons. Reprinted by permission of G.P. Putnam's Sons.

"The Tortoise and the Hare," by Tom Paxton, from *Aesop's Fables*, illustrated by Robert Rayevsky. Text copyright © 1988 by Tom Paxton. Illustrations copyright © 1988 by Robert Rayevsky. Reprinted by permission of Morrow Jr. Books (a division of William Morrow & Co.) and Wendy Lipkind Agency.

"Whistles," by Dorothy Aldis, from *Here, There and Everywhere*. Copyright 1927, 1928, copyright © renewed 1955, 1956 by Dorothy Aldis. Reprinted by permission of G.P. Putnam's Sons.

"A Year Later," in *Hello and Good-By*, by Mary Ann Hoberman. Copyright © 1959 by Mary Ann Hoberman, renewed 1987. Reprinted by permission of the Gina Maccoby Literary Agency.

Quotations from Authors/Illustrators

Patricia Reilly Giff, page 74, from *Something About the Author*, vol. 33. Copyright © 1983 by Gale Research Inc. Reprinted by permission of the publisher.

Theme Books

The Theme Books shown on Extended Reading pages are available from Houghton Mifflin Company and are reprinted with permission from various publishers. Jacket artists for these books are listed below.

Molly and the Slow Teeth, by Pat Ross. Jacket art by Jerry Milord, copyright © 1980 by Jerome E. Milord.

Mouse Soup, by Arnold Lobel. Jacket art by Arnold Lobel, copyright © 1977 by Arnold Lobel.

Once in a Wood: Ten Tales from Aesop, by Eve Rice. Jacket art by Eve Rice, copyright © 1979 by Eve Rice.

The Quicksand Book, by Tomie dePaola. Jacket art by Tomie dePaola, copyright © 1977 by Tomie dePaola.